DESIGN & TECHNOLOGY

The Process

Colin Chapman
Advisory Teacher for Design & Technology

Val Charles
Advisory Teacher for Business Education

Mike Finney
Head of Technology,
William Farr C of E Comprehensive School, Welton

Michael Horsley
Advisory Teacher for Information Technology

Heather Jeffrey
Head of Home Economics,
King Edward VI School, Louth

Malcolm Moyes
Head of Learning Resources,
Kesteven & Sleaford High School for Girls

CollinsEducational
An imprint of HarperCollinsPublishers

Published in 1992 by CollinsEducational
An imprint of HarperCollins*Publishers*
77-85 Fulham Palace Road
Hammersmith
London W6 8JB

ISBN 0 00 322061 3

Designed by Ken Vail Graphic Design,
(Production management Glennis Starling)

Cover design by Raynor Design
Cover photograph by Chris Gilbert

Illustrated by Ann Baum, Katy Bradbury, Tim Cooke,
Dalton/Jacobs Illustration, Helen Herbert, David Lock,
Malcolm Ryan
Location photographs by Peter Sharp, Studio 7; and
Nicola Cornish
Picture research by Caroline Mitchell

Printed and bound in Hong Kong

Commissioning Editor: Graham Bradbury
Project Editor: Philippa Moyle
Editor: Katherine King
Production: Ken Ruskin

CONTENTS

WHAT'S THIS BOOK ABOUT ?

This book is called *Design & Technology: The Process*. It begins by telling you what Design & Technology is and then goes on to show you how to go about designing and making things yourself.

Design & Technology is not simply about using materials to produce a product. You have to think very carefully about what is needed before you start to make anything. Design & Technology is really about finding out what is needed and then designing and making a product to meet this need.

Artefacts, systems and environments

The products you design can be divided into three groups: **artefacts**, **systems** and **environments**.

Artefacts
These are objects which have been made, such as meals, toys and clothes.

Systems
These are formed when a number of artefacts, or elements, are put together to perform a task. A computer is an example of a system. It consists of a keyboard, a monitor and a disk drive. The process used to design things in Design & Technology is also a system.

Environments
These are your surroundings. The room you are in now, and the world you live in, are both examples of environments.

Some of the products you are likely to design and make may well fit into more than one of these groups. A motor car can be seen as an artefact but it is also a collection of systems. It has a steering system, a braking system and an electrical system. The interior of the car also creates an environment for the driver and the passengers.

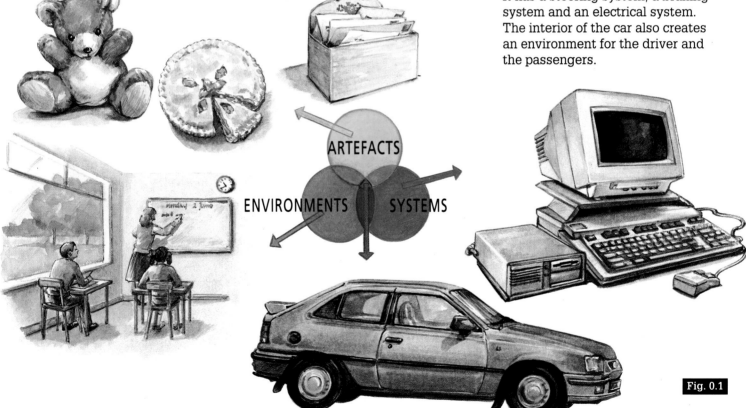

ARTEFACTS

ENVIRONMENTS   SYSTEMS

Fig. 0.1

EXTRAS

Extras are challenges to encourage you to find out more about Design & Technology. Try this Extra now. Look at the things around you. Can you put them into groups under the headings Artefacts, Systems and Environments? Do some of them fit into more than one group?

Materials

Making things in Design & Technology will usually involve using lots of different **materials**, sometimes on their own and sometimes together. These materials include food, textiles, clay, wood, metal, plastic, paper and card. As you learn more about the materials, you will be expected to choose the most suitable ones for your design work. There is no limit to the type of materials you can use but they must be appropriate for what you are going to make.

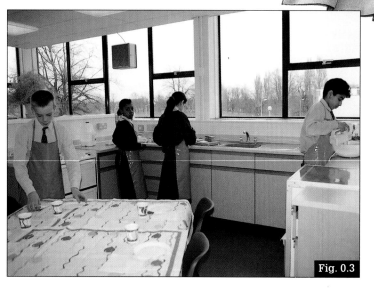

Fig. 0.2 Examples of the materials used in Design & Technology

Fig. 0.3

Teamwork

For much of the work that you will do in Design & Technology you will be finding things out for yourself. You may be working on your own or you may be working in a group. Working with other people is very important. Designers in industry rarely work alone – they are usually part of a design team.

You will be expected to use what you have learned in other subjects in school. English, maths and science are very important, and provide you with some of the basic skills which you will need to use.

Contexts, topics and tasks

Your Design & Technology activities will involve you in thinking about areas that are familiar to you, such as your home, your school or your recreation. As you progress, you will be encouraged to be more adventurous and look at areas that are new to you, such as the community, or business and industry. These are all **contexts** for your Design & Technology activities and are shown in Fig. 0.4.

A Design & Technology activity may begin by asking you to explore a context like 'the home', or you may be given a **topic** such as 'your room'. This is a topic that is within the context of the home. It is a starting point for Design & Technology. From this starting point you will be able to identify specific **tasks** to carry out.

SCHOOL

HOME

RECREATION

THE COMMUNITY

BUSINESS AND INDUSTRY

Fig. 0.4 Contexts for Design & Technology activities

The design process

IDENTIFYING NEEDS AND OPPORTUNITIES

GENERATING A DESIGN

PLANNING AND MAKING

EVALUATING

Fig. 0.5
The design process

Designing products is not difficult once you know what to do. If you were sent on an errand to a place that you had not been to before you would probably be given a map marked with a route. The design process that you are going to work through in Design & Technology is really a route for you to follow. It will give you a framework to work within and help you to make some of the decisions that will need to be made.

Fig. 0.5 shows the design process as a line. This is to make it easier to understand to begin with. In fact, it is more like a circular process (see Fig. 0.6). Once you have made something, and it has been evaluated, you could go through the whole process again and improve your design. You could carry on working on a design in this way until you are satisfied with it. You may be given a product that already exists to evaluate. This will be the starting point for your design activity. For example, your teacher may ask you to test a simple product and then see if you can improve it.

The titles of the four stages of the design process are very broad headings which describe generally what takes place. The chapters of this book will take you through the design process, describing each stage in more detail.

The design process is not only used in schools. Designers and engineers use very similar processes to help them with their work on projects in industry. The process of designing is, therefore, very important.

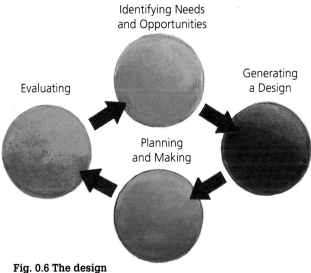

Fig. 0.6 The design
process seen as a circle

1 OPPORTUNITIES FOR DESIGNING

Design & Technology is about identifying a need and then designing and making a product to meet this need. The first stage of the design process, therefore, is to find out what is needed. This is known as identifying needs and opportunities.

Needs

Everyone has needs. People need air, water, food, warmth and shelter. These are basic physical needs and without them you cannot survive. People have emotional needs, too – they need to be wanted, to feel safe and secure, to feel a sense of achievement and to be part of the community. Human needs is a complex topic – different people have different needs depending on their situation.

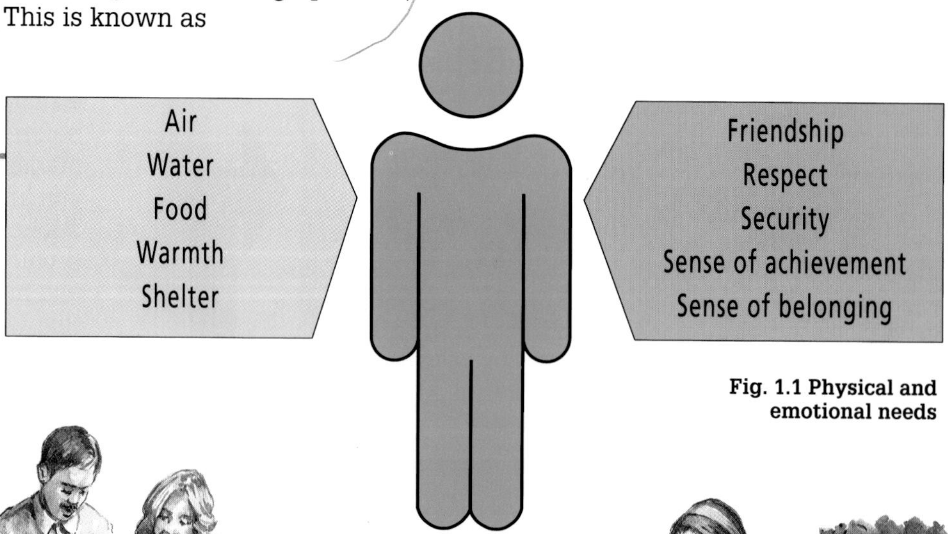

Your needs may be similar to those of your classmates but they will be different from the needs of your parents. As people get older their needs change. Babies, teenagers and elderly people all have very different needs.

People with disabilities have the same physical and emotional needs as anyone else but they also have special needs according to their disability. People from other countries and different cultures also have different needs. The needs of people in developing countries are very different from the needs of people who live in some parts of Western Europe. Needs in the developing world are usually more concerned with food, shelter and safety. In industrial societies, such as Britain, these needs are usually met and taken for granted. People's needs in these countries are more likely to be related to comfort, convenience and fashion.

Air
Water
Food
Warmth
Shelter

Friendship
Respect
Security
Sense of achievement
Sense of belonging

Fig. 1.1 Physical and emotional needs

Fig. 1.2 Different people have different needs

In D & T, you will learn to:
know the importance of exploring needs and opportunities before proposing solutions

Over the years, people's needs have changed and things that were considered to be important in the past are, perhaps, not as important today. Fifty years ago, most people's need for transport was met by buses and trains. Nowadays, many people have their own personal forms of transport – most families have at least one car. The need now is for better roads and for vehicles which cause less harm to the environment.

Opportunities

Meeting people's individual needs may provide obvious opportunities for designing but there are many other opportunities as well. Identifying these opportunities, however, is not always easy.

Looking closely at an existing product, which can be an artefact, system or environment, can provide new opportunities for design work. If an artefact does not work very well, it may be possible to modify it so that it works more efficiently. Reorganising the way that something is done may involve designing a new system. Redesigning or redecorating a room can create a whole new environment. Fig. 1.3 shows a room which could provide many opportunities for designing.

Fig. 1.3

Fig. 1.4 Changes in design

Many products have been restyled during their lifetime to allow them to keep pace with fashion trends. Other products have been redesigned to enable them to make use of modern technology. Telephones are a good example of this as they have changed a great deal in recent years. They are now smaller, more compact and often include such things as memories and timers. The body of the telephone has become much smaller but the handset remains almost unchanged. This is because the earpiece and the microphone in the handset must be positioned a fixed distance apart, in order for the telephone to work properly. On some models, it has been possible to put the push buttons into the handset but the position of the earpiece and the microphone still determines the overall design of the telephone.

It is very important that you fully understand the need before you begin to design a product. You must make sure that a real need exists. In 1985, Sir Clive Sinclair identified a need for cheap personal transport, and he designed a battery-powered tricycle, called a C5. Unfortunately, Sir Clive did not take into account the emotional needs of the person using the C5. It was unsuccessful because many people felt silly and unsafe while sitting in it. Remember that a successful design is one which fully meets the need.

Fig. 1.5 The C5

EXTRAS

1. Study Fig. 1.3. in detail. Write down as many opportunities for designing as you can find.

Activities

DESIGN & TECHNOLOGY	NAME	CLASS
Identifying the needs of pupils at a new school  For many pupils, arriving at a new school can be an unsettling experience. Try and remember how you felt on your first day at your current school. For example, did you feel excited, nervous, worried or even scared? Many of the problems that new pupils face are concerned with identity - identifying people and property. You may find it hard to remember the names of all your teachers and the members of your class. It may also be difficult to identify your own property - how will you know which of the 160 identical Design & Technology folders is yours? Write down a list of products you could make to meet these needs.	**Products to design** Choose a product that you would like to make from your above list. Then write a design brief for this product. **Design brief**	**Analysis** Try and answer the following questions. 1. Which materials will you be able to use for your product? 2. What size will your product be? 3. How much time will there be to make the product? 4. Can you think of anything else which needs to be thought about at this stage?

Fig. 1.6 A worksheet for a controlled activity

You will be able to identify needs and opportunities through various activities. You may begin with **controlled** activities and then move on to **directed** and **open** activities.

Controlled activities

To begin with, your teacher may identify the needs for you, and present you with a task to carry out. It could be a specific task which asks you to design something to solve a problem that you have been given. These tasks are known as controlled activities. You will probably be given a worksheet, like the one shown in Fig. 1.6, which identifies the needs and tells you what to do.

Directed activities

As you become more familiar with the design process, you will be expected to begin to identify needs and opportunities for yourself. Your teacher will probably give you a starting point and then let you carry on from there.

Fig. 1.7

Design Brief

I am going to design and make something to help me to identify my new Design & Technology folder.

In D&T, you will learn to:
devise an effective strategy for investigating a specific situation

The starting point can vary from visits to places of interest to people coming to your school to talk to you about their needs or problems.

When you fully understand the situation, and have found out what the needs are, you can write down what you are going to design. This is called the **design brief**. It is a simple statement of what you intend to do and might begin with the words 'I am going to design and make a ...'. Try to keep your brief short and to the point. It does not really need to be more than one or two sentences (see Fig. 1.7).

Sometimes, existing products are used as a starting point. You may well be given a familiar object, such as a hair dryer or a telephone, and asked to study it in order to find out what its strengths and weaknesses are. You can then write a design brief for the redesign of the product. You must make sure that you identify the original needs and try to meet them in your new design.

Open activities

It is always much more exciting to meet 'real' needs than to meet simulated (artificial) ones. Open activities make this possible. They allow you to identify needs which you have yourself. For example, you may have needs which come from your hobbies or interests.

You will be responsible for most of the decisions which will have to be made during open activities. Your teacher's role will be to guide you through the process and help you with any problems.

Techniques

You will need to investigate in order to identify opportunities for designing. Some useful techniques for investigating are listed here. There is more information on investigating in chapter 2.

Fig. 1.8

Observations

Observing is an excellent technique for identifying needs and opportunities. There may well be a dangerous situation outside your school at the end of the afternoon. School buses and parents' cars will probably be arriving as pupils are leaving. Observing this situation will make you more aware of the problems and provide you with some excellent opportunities for designing. The result of your work may not be an artefact – it is more likely to be a system which will improve the situation outside the school entrance.

Interviews

Interviewing is another useful technique for gaining information about a particular situation. However, you will have to be able to separate facts from opinions. Facts are true statements while opinions are people's personal views. You must try to remember that facts and opinions are very different. (For more information on interviews see page 21.)

Market research

When professional designers begin to think about new products, they carry out an investigation to find out what the needs are and what people really want. They often employ people called market researchers to do this for them. **Market research** involves collecting and recording information. This is usually done by asking people questions and writing their answers on a special form called a **questionnaire**. (There is more information on using questionnaires on page 21.) Real market research can be an expensive exercise but it is quite possible for you to carry out similar research yourself to identify needs for your design work. (Market research is covered in more detail in *Design & Technology: Techniques and Resources*.)

Recording

The data that you have gathered will need to be organised and recorded properly if it is going to be of any real use to you. It may be possible to enter it on to a computer database where it can be sorted, stored, and later used to produce graphs or pie charts.

Observations that you have made can be recorded with a video camera. Video recordings are very useful as you can replay the tape and freeze the action while you study it in detail. It is also useful to tape-record interviews. You will have to remember that some people may be a little nervous or apprehensive about being recorded so don't forget to ask their permission first.

Fig. 1.9 A video camera

Case studies

The different data that you have collected can be put together to form a **case study**. This consists of written, graphic or tape-recorded information about a particular topic. Case studies can provide you with a number of different opportunities for designing. (For examples of case studies, see page 18.)

EXTRAS

1. Going to a new school for the first time can provide many opportunities for design activities. Think back to your first day at your current school. In a group, discuss what your needs were then and make a list of them.

2. Think about your hobbies and your interests. Write down any opportunities for design activities that they provide.

A Starting Point for Design Activities – The Enviropark

Fig. 1.10 shows a map of an 'Enviropark' which has been prepared by a Design & Technology teacher in order to provide a starting point for a variety of open design activities. It shows the grounds of a large country house which are being turned into a theme park. The park is designed to encourage people to explore the natural environment. The park will rely on visitors for its income but much needs to be done before it can open its gates to the public.

The aims of the Enviropark

1. To help people to learn about, understand and experience the natural environment.

2. To develop people's awareness of environmental issues.

3. To be informative and entertaining, and provide something to interest each member of the family.

4. To provide the right facilities to make a visit to the park 'a good day out'.

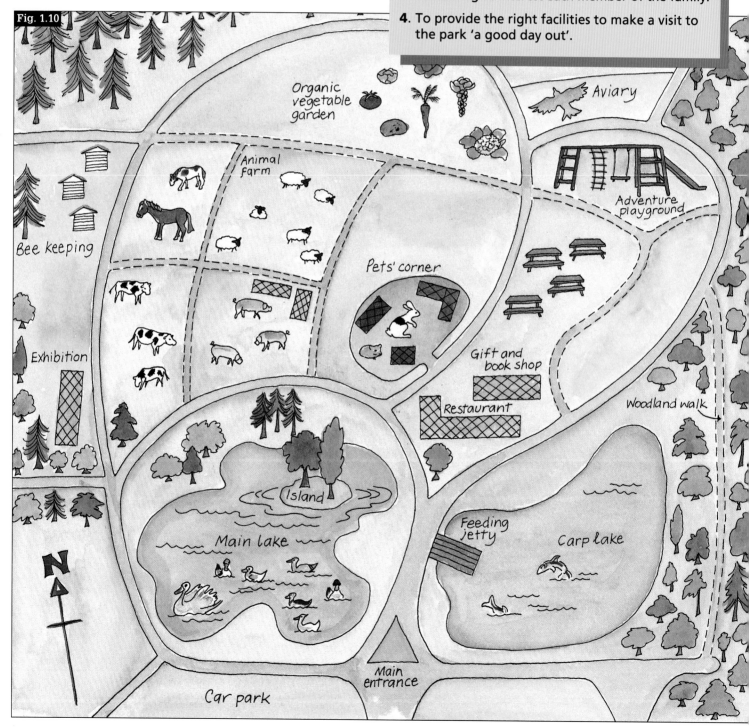

Fig. 1.10

The pupils have studied the map and the aims of the park. They have identified a number of opportunities for design activities.

▲ Tom has decided to design a poster and a leaflet to advertise and promote the park.

▲ Sarah and Junior have decided to design logos which can be printed on to T-shirts. These can then be sold as souvenirs in the gift shop.

▲ Nathalie has decided to look at the facilities needed for people with disabilities.

▲ Lee and Anouska have decided that a bird-feeding system is needed in the aviary.

▲ Michelle has decided that the park needs signs to help the visitors find their way around.

Things to think about

It is a good idea to try to think about the things that other people are likely to need when they visit the park. You could decide to carry out a survey to find out people's needs. You might like to consider how and why people will be attracted to the park and how they will find out about it. Don't forget to consider the needs of the people living nearby. Is the park likely to create problems for them?

You will probably find it helpful to discuss your ideas in a group. As you discuss them, make a list of all the ideas. This will be useful later when you have to make a decision about what you are going to design. Sketches and notes are a simple but effective way of recording your ideas.

EXTRAS

1. Study the map of the Enviropark carefully. Write down as many opportunities for design activities as you can find. Then write a design brief for one of the design activities that you have identified.

▲ Kamal has decided to investigate the adventure playground as a starting point for his activity.

Design Opportunities from Existing Products

Looking at an existing product, which can be an artefact, a system or an environment, can provide many opportunities for designing. It may be possible to modify an artefact, or improve a system or an environment in some way. In order to do this, you will need to carry out some form of evaluation (sometimes called an appraisal). You can then use the information you find to help you in your design activity.

Evaluations

An evaluation involves making a careful study of the product in order to find out how successful or effective it is. It is a good idea to draw up a list of things to test it against. You could consider questions like how well it works, how safe it is and whether it harms the environment in any way. You may need to talk to other people who have used the product and record their comments and views on it. If you think about it carefully, you should be able to work out what the original needs were. Then you can check to see if they have been met by the finished product. (For more information on evaluating see chapter 6.)

The outcome of your evaluation could lead your design activity into one of several directions. You may decide, for example, that the original designers have met the needs successfully and, in your view, the product cannot be improved. However, it is more likely that you will be able to make modifications because needs, materials and technology change very quickly during the life of a product. Following your evaluation, you may feel that the original design is totally unsuitable to meet the needs and that the product must be completely redesigned.

In D&T, you will learn to:
investigate artefacts, systems and environments to find ideas for new designs
use information and experience gained from appraising products

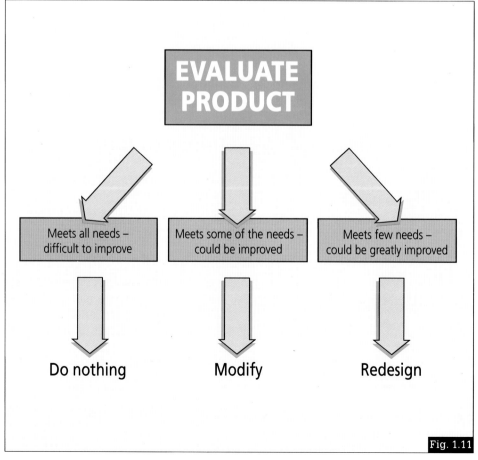

Fig. 1.11

ARTEFACTS

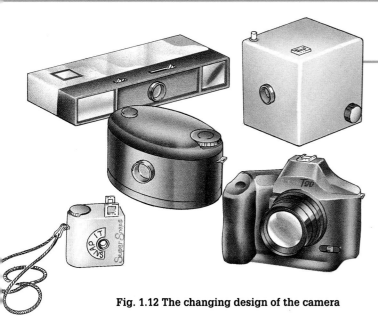

Fig. 1.12 The changing design of the camera

The camera is an artefact that has provided many opportunities for designing over the years. It has been modified many times and, in some cases, redesigned completely to involve the use of modern technology and more suitable materials. The body of the camera was originally made from wood and leather but it has since been made from steel, aluminium and, more recently, a form of plastic known as polycarbonate. Style plays an important part in the design of products. Many products have been redesigned in order to keep up with changing styles and fashions. A product which looks good will appeal to people and is, therefore, more likely to sell than an unattractive product. Over the years, the camera has changed from a simple box to a very stylish, highly technical product.

Do you have a storage problem with tapes and compact discs? It is a common problem which many people share. Tapes and compact discs are expensive to buy and need to be looked after properly. They can easily be damaged accidentally, especially if they are left in the hot sun for any length of time. They also need to be protected from dust and dirt and should not be left near anything which is magnetic. Their storage system needs to be adaptable and portable, especially if you want to listen to your music out of doors or in a car. Discuss your own needs for the storage of your tapes and compact discs in a group and then make a list of these needs. Look at the products shown in Fig. 1.13 and see if any of them meet your needs. You need to consider the following questions: Are they adaptable? Which ones are portable? Can they be added to as your music collection gets bigger? By thinking about your needs and evaluating these products, it should be possible for you to write a design brief for a product to solve your storage problem.

Fig. 1.13 Solutions to tape and CD storage problems

While evaluating a product, you may find other opportunities for designing. Make a note of these, as you may be able to follow them up later. Open activities allow you to 'follow your nose' and go where your work leads you.

SYSTEMS

Existing systems can provide opportunities for designing in the same way as artefacts. A system is something which consists of a number of artefacts, or elements, put together to perform a task. Changing one of the elements has an effect on the other elements in the system.

Your school timetable is an example of quite a complicated system. If you were to change part of it, it would certainly have an effect on the rest of the system. Organising the school timetable is a complicated process which provides plenty of problem-solving opportunities, such as making sure that there are enough specialist subject teachers and rooms available when needed.

Fig. 1.14 An example of a system

Period \ Day	1	2	3	4	5	6	7	8
MON	DrT RM12 ←→ Mr Bradbury		English RM11 Mrs Moyle	French RM4 Mrs Sawyer	Science RM2 ←→ Mrs Green		Maths RM7 Mr Woods	French RM4 Mrs Sawyer
TUES	English RM11 Mrs Moyle	Music RM10 Mr Greves	French RM4 Mrs Sawyer	Maths RM7 Mr Woods	Art RM14 ←→ Mrs Durdin		English RM3 Mrs Moyle	Science RM2 Mrs Green
WED	Science RM2 ←→ Mrs Green		Geography RM1 ←→ Mr Singh		Maths RM7 Mr Woods	P.E. Miss Harris	R.E. RM9 Miss King	History RM5 Miss Mortimer
THUR	History RM5 ←→ Miss Mortimer		R.E. RM9 Miss King	Geography RM1 Mr Singh	DoT RM12 ←→ Miss Smith		P.E. ←→ Miss Harris	
FRI	English RM3 ←→ Mrs Moyle		P.E. Miss Harris	Maths RM7 Mr Woods	French RM4 Mrs Sawyer	Music RM10 Mr Greves	Drama RM6 Mr Duke	Maths RM7 Mr Woods

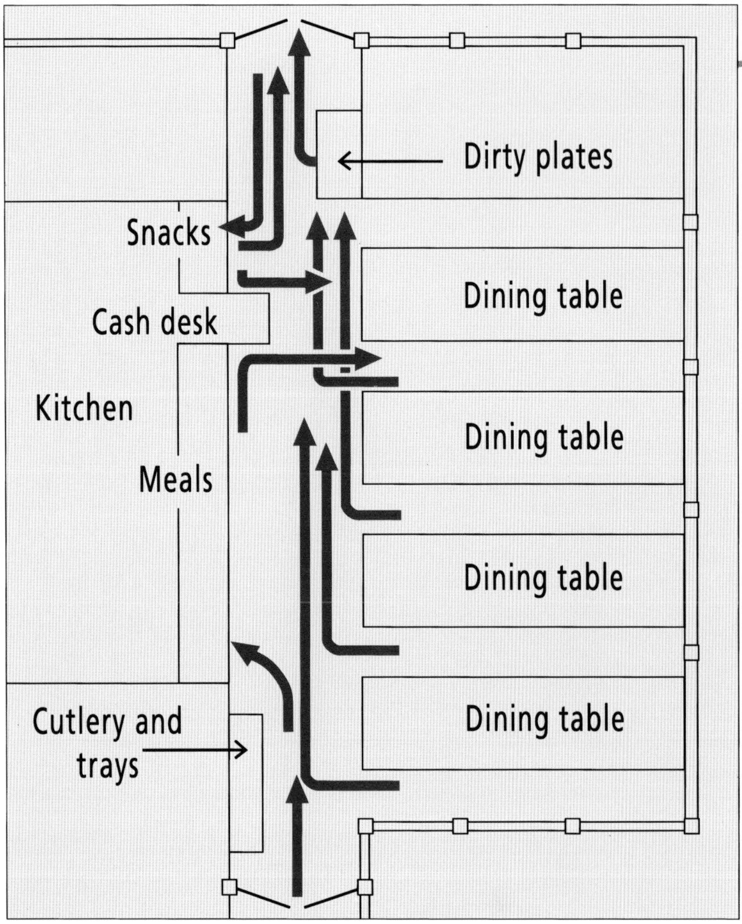

A school meals system

Your school probably has a system for feeding pupils at lunchtime. Evaluating such a school meals system can provide many opportunities for designing. However, this would be a major task if you were to consider all of it. Various systems are involved, such as menu planning, kitchen organisation and hygiene, as well as feeding large numbers of young people in a short time. It is worth remembering that a school meals service is run as a business in many schools. This means that they have to make a profit from the food they sell in order to pay the wages of the meals staff and the electricity and gas bills. Your evaluation may show that there are opportunities for business and economic activities.

Your design activities may not involve redesigning the actual system. Instead, you may find that artefacts are required to help the existing system to run more efficiently. These could include cutlery storage, some way of dealing with leftovers or a method of dispensing disposable cups. You may also feel that improvements to the environment of the dining hall and the kitchen are necessary in order to improve the system further.

Fig. 1.15 A school meals system

ENVIRONMENTS

Environments can also provide many opportunities for designing. Some topics involve the environment in general, while others involve your personal environment. As Fig. 1.3 on page 9 shows, your own room can provide opportunities for designing.

A garden environment

Gardens provide environments which can be enjoyed, especially in the spring and summer. Some people like to relax in the garden, while others get a great deal of pleasure from working in the garden. Creating new gardens and looking after established ones will provide you with many opportunities for designing.

Fig. 1.16

Fig. 1.17

A working environment

An environment can have a great effect on people, especially when they are at work. The area where you work is known as your working environment. For some people this might be a factory, an office or a shop. Your own working environment will either be your classroom or the room where you do your homework. Consider the following questions about your present environment. Do you feel comfortable as you read this book? Does the room you are in create a pleasant environment for work? Are the chairs or stools comfortable? Does the colour scheme of the room make you feel relaxed? Are you warm? Questions like these are important to consider because your working environment affects the way you work.

Fig. 1.18

A home environment

Many people like to alter their home environment quite often by decorating or changing their furnishings. When decorating, the choice of colour is very important. Certain colours, such as yellow and red, make a room appear to feel warmer while other colours, such as blue and green, have the opposite effect. One style of furnishing may create a formal environment while another may create a more informal environment. The home environment, therefore, provides many different opportunities for designing.

EXTRAS

1. Fig. 1.15 shows the plan of a school's dining hall and kitchen. Study it carefully and write down as many opportunities for designing as you can find.

Case Studies as a Starting Point

Case studies, like the ones on this page, can form a good starting point for design activities. In a group, study the information given in each of the case studies. For each study, work out what the needs are and suggest design activities that will meet these needs. Then write a design brief for each activity.

Tracey and Kaseem

Tracey and Kaseem are 11 and are going to secondary school next term. They have visited the school several times and everyone seems very friendly. It is a very large school and Kaseem is worried that he will get lost and be late for lessons. Tracey is worried about remembering all the things that she has to take to school with her. She is also afraid that she might lose her new sports kit and trainers.

Market Benton windmill

Market Benton windmill was in ruins from the 1920s until last year when its restoration was completed. It took a team of volunteers over ten years to rebuild the windmill at a cost of around £15,000. It is now open every weekend and bank holiday, except Christmas and New Year. Visitors can pay fifty pence to climb to the top of the windmill and enjoy the views over the surrounding countryside. They can also buy flour which has been traditionally ground. The volunteers who run the windmill estimate that it costs in the region of £3,500 each year to maintain it.

Holmes Farm Park

Several years ago, Mr Holmes began to find that his small farm was no longer profitable. He had the idea of turning it into a farm park. Now people from the town visit the farm, pick their own fruit and vegetables and see the animals. This year, Mr Holmes has stocked his lake with fish, and has made plans to build an adventure playground. He hopes that many more people will visit the farm this year.

Mr and Mrs Green

Mr and Mrs Green have retired and are now in their late sixties. Their children are grown up, and have left home. The Greens have decided to move to a small one-bedroomed bungalow. They both enjoy gardening very much but Mrs Green suffers from arthritis and Mr Green has a heart condition which prevents him from doing any heavy digging or lifting.

Mrs Johnson

Mrs Johnson suffers from a rare disease which has caused her to lose her sight. She lives in a ground floor flat with her guide dog, Sam. She is visited by her daughter once or twice a week and she usually has Sunday lunch with her son and his family. Although Mrs Johnson has begun to get used to being blind, and can find her way around the flat, she still has some problems in the kitchen. She finds many simple tasks very difficult and is frustrated at not being able to do everything for herself.

2 INVESTIGATING

You will need to investigate at various stages during the design process. It is particularly necessary at the start when you are identifying needs and opportunities. You may also need to investigate later while drawing up your specification and developing your design proposal. Your investigation will involve you in collecting information from many different sources.

One way of collecting information is to interview people or conduct a survey using a questionnaire. This is called collecting information from a **primary source** because it is collected first-hand by you. You will probably find that it is not always possible to find out everything for yourself. You may have to refer to information already collected by other people. This is called collecting information from a **secondary source**.

QUESTIONNAIRES
LETTERS
BOOKS
THE MEDIA
TAPE RECORDINGS
VIDEOTEX
COMPUTER DATABASES
BRAINSTORMING SESSIONS
CD-ROMS
INTERVIEWS

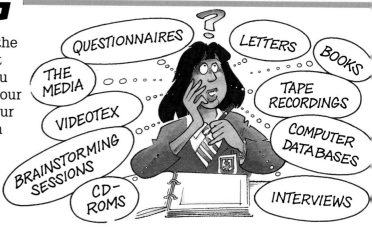

As you investigate, you should keep the topic you are investigating clearly in mind. This will help you to keep your research to the point and prevent it from becoming too wide ranging.

Brainstorming

If you are working in a group, you may find it useful to have a **brainstorming** session. This is a good way of finding out other people's ideas about a topic. When you organise a brainstorming session you may find it useful to follow the simple rules shown in Fig. 2.1.

Brainstorming rules

Fig. 2.1

1. Choose someone to record the ideas that are suggested. They can be written on a flip chart, a chalkboard or on a large sheet of paper.
2. Write down everything that the group can think of that is related to the topic. Remember that any idea is worth writing down at this stage.
3. Don't be tempted to discuss the ideas as you think of them. Write them down first and discuss them later.
4. Try to prevent the brainstorming session from going on too long. Set a time in which to work – 15 to 20 minutes should be long enough.

Spider diagrams

Spider diagrams are a useful way of recording a brainstorming session. Begin by writing the topic in the centre of the page and then write each idea around it. You could draw a line to link each idea to the topic. This will help you later if it becomes a large or complicated diagram. Allow the diagram to grow as ideas are recorded.

Fig. 2.2 shows a spider diagram produced by a group of pupils brainstorming the topic of festivals and celebrations. Once they had recorded their ideas, they evaluated them and chose the particular festivals that they wanted to concentrate on in their design work – Christmas and New Year. Fig. 2.3 shows a spider diagram of their ideas for these festivals.

FESTIVALS AND CELEBRATIONS
CHRISTMAS
NEW YEAR
ANNIVERSARIES
RAMADAN
LENT
MAY DAY
EASTER
MOTHER'S DAY FATHER'S DAY
BONFIRE NIGHT
HARVEST FESTIVAL
DIWALI
BIRTHDAYS
SAINTS' DAYS
PANCAKE DAY
NICHOLAS VALENTINE GEORGE
HALLOWE'EN
HOLI
WEDDINGS
SOLSTICES
SALAH

Fig. 2.2

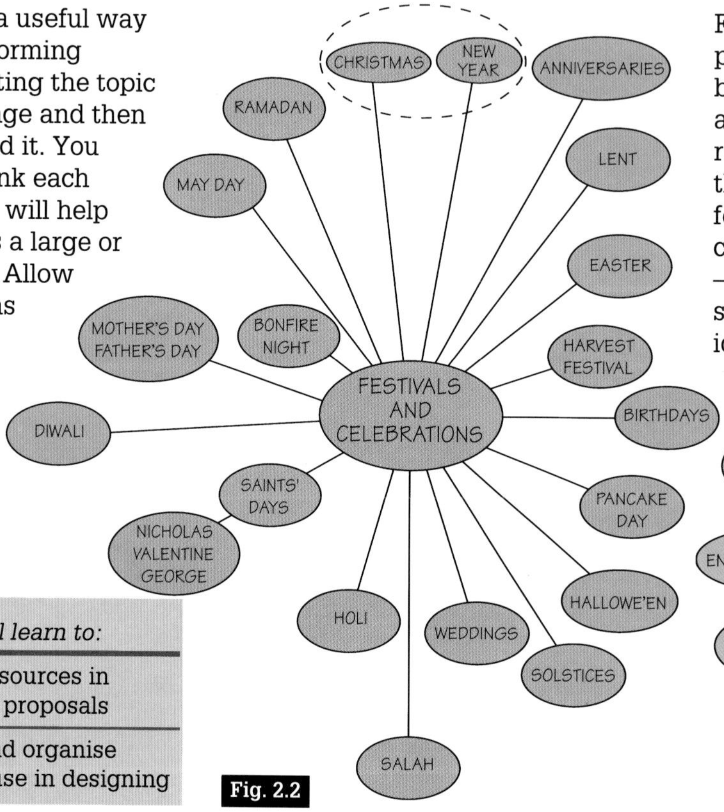

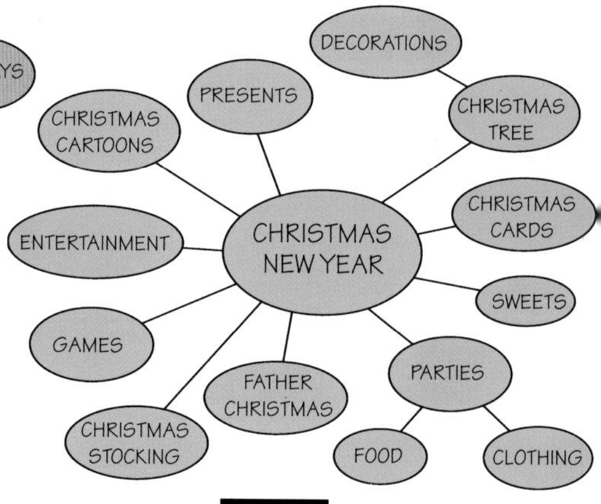

CHRISTMAS NEW YEAR
DECORATIONS
PRESENTS
CHRISTMAS CARTOONS
CHRISTMAS TREE
CHRISTMAS CARDS
ENTERTAINMENT
SWEETS
GAMES
PARTIES
FATHER CHRISTMAS
CHRISTMAS STOCKING
FOOD
CLOTHING

Fig. 2.3

In D&T, you will learn to:

- use information sources in developing your proposals
- gather, select and organise information for use in designing

Primary Sources

When you collect information from primary sources, you will need to ask questions – for example, during an **interview** or when using a **questionnaire**. Questions will enable you to find out what other people think and feel about your particular topic. You should work out exactly what information you want to find out, and then word your questions accordingly. Interviews are usually undertaken when you want to find out individual people's views, while questionnaires are used to find out information from larger groups of people.

Interviews

If you wish to interview someone, it is polite to ask if you can arrange a convenient time and place to meet. You should introduce yourself and explain the reason for the interview. You must always try to word your questions carefully and sensibly, so that you do not offend anyone.

Fig. 2.4

Questionnaires

When carrying out a survey using a questionnaire you will need a fairly large number of people in order to get enough useful information. Depending on your topic, you may need to target a particular age group. Designing a questionnaire needs a little thought and care, if it is to be worthwhile. Always try to ask simple questions first, and then progress on to more difficult ones. Questions which require one word answers, such as yes or no, are called **closed questions**. Questions which require more detailed answers are called **open questions**. (For information on analysing the results of interviews and questionnaires see page 25.)

In order for the information you collect to be useful you must find out a little about the person you are questioning – for example, you will need to record their age and sex. Always remember to thank people for helping you. If you are polite, you will be pleasantly surprised to find how willing adults are to help you with your work.

```
┌─ Fig. 2.5 ──────────────────────────────────────────┐
│              LOST PROPERTY SURVEY                     │
│  NAME _____         │
│  MALE  ☐      FEMALE  ☐                               │
│  SCHOOL YEAR      7 ☐    8 ☐    9 ☐   10 ☐   11 ☐    │
│  HAVE YOU EVER LOST ANYTHING AT SCHOOL?               │
│                         YES ☐      NO ☐               │
│  WHAT HAVE YOU LOST?     BOOKS  ☐    MONEY ☐          │
│                          CLOTHING ☐   BAGS  ☐         │
│  WAS THE LOST ITEM  RETURNED TO YOU?                  │
│                         YES ☐      NO ☐               │
│  HOW WAS IT RETURNED?                                 │
│  FOUND BY YOU   ☐      LOST PROPERTY  ☐               │
│  CARETAKER      ☐      OTHER          ☐               │
│  IF OTHER, GIVE DETAILS _____       │
│  _____         │
│  _____         │
└──────────────────────────────────────────────────────┘
```

Asking the experts

Carrying out an investigation may mean that you need to contact people who are experts on the particular topic that you are working on. This could involve designers and manufacturers. You will probably need to write or telephone in order to make your first contact with them. Letters may take longer to get a reply but they have the advantage that a copy can be kept in your folder. It is a good idea to show your letters to your teacher before you post them. Find out if there is a fax machine in your school office as your teacher may be able to allow you to use it. A fax combines the advantages of a letter with the speed of a telephone. Once you have made contact with the relevant person you may be invited to visit them. This will give you the opportunity to see places like factories, offices and playgroups for yourself.

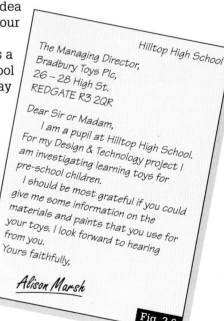

Hilltop High School

The Managing Director,
Bradbury Toys Plc,
26 – 28 High St.
REDGATE R3 2QR

Dear Sir or Madam,
I am a pupil at Hilltop High School. For my Design & Technology project I am investigating learning toys for pre-school children.
I should be most grateful if you could give me some information on the materials and paints that you use for your toys. I look forward to hearing from you.
Yours faithfully,

Alison Marsh

Fig. 2.6

Secondary Sources

If you know where to look, researching information from secondary sources can be quicker and easier than finding out everything for yourself.

Fig. 2.7

Resource areas in school

Your first secondary source of information will be the books and resources in your Design & Technology department. These will include leaflets, posters, catalogues and magazines. Don't forget to ask your Design & Technology teachers. They will be able to direct you towards the information that you need and suggest other sources for you to try. Most topics in Design & Technology cross the boundaries of your school subjects, and you may need to visit the resource areas of other subjects such as science, geography or history.

Fig. 2.8

Using the library

The next important secondary source of information is your school library or local public library. Books and information in libraries are catalogued according to the Dewey system. If you are not familiar with the system, ask the librarian to help you. It is usually possible to look up information either by subject or, if you know the book you want, by its title or author. Libraries usually have a good reference section where you can find dictionaries, directories and encyclopaedias as well as general reference material. Normally, you will not be allowed to borrow reference books so you will have to make notes from them in the library. Many libraries are now making use of Information Technology and it is possible to find information directly from computer databases.

Museums and exhibitions

Museums display a considerable amount of information which has often been gathered over many years. You may be lucky enough to live near a museum or an exhibition hall where displays and exhibitions are regularly held. Seeing how particular designs have developed can be very interesting and useful for your design work. Your local Museums Service may be able to loan exhibits to your school or set up displays for you. You could discuss this with your teacher.

Computer databases

A **database** is a collection of information stored on a computer. The information you want can be recalled from the database and it can be updated if required. There is probably a database in your Design & Technology department at school which contains details of all the materials and components that are available for you to use. Some databases are especially designed for Design & Technology. They allow you to list the materials that you need for a particular product and then estimate the total cost. This information is very useful when you are planning a project.

Fig. 2.9

CD-ROMs

Compact discs (CDs) were originally used to store data which could then be replayed as music. Now they can also be used to store pictures and information which can be played back through a computer. These are called **CD-ROMs** (see Fig. 2.10). The data is stored on the disk and is 'read' by a laser beam. The computer converts the data to a picture which is displayed on the screen. A vast amount of information can be stored on a CD-ROM which makes it a very useful source of information.

Fig. 2.10

Videotex

Information stored on a computer can be sent by telephone line or television signals to a computer monitor or television screen where it is displayed. This is known as a **videotex system**. There are two main types of videotex in use at present – **viewdata** and **teletext**.

Viewdata

The largest viewdata system in Britain is British Telecom's Prestel service. It is used by many schools and businesses, such as travel agents, banks and insurance companies. The user's computers are connected by telephone to large regional computers which store a vast amount of information in a database. It is possible to look through the pages, load the required information into your own computer and then print it out. Some schools are linked by another viewdata service called The Times Network System (TTNS) and other schools use another on-line database called Campus 2000.

Teletext

Teletext is a simpler system than viewdata as information is only sent one way. The information is broadcast by normal television signals and can be received by television sets fitted with special decoders. There are two teletext services available at present – Ceefax, broadcast by the BBC, and Oracle, broadcast by ITV. Teletext services provide up-to-date information on a wide range of subjects.

Fig. 2.11 Oracle's weather map

The media

The media includes television, radio, newspapers and magazines, all of which are good sources of general information. There are many television programmes that deal with social and environmental issues, and documentaries which explore a wide range of topics that may be useful for your design work. Programmes made especially for schools may be useful, too. Your Design & Technology resource area may have a collection of videotapes which you could use to record a programme. The radio, newspapers and magazines are also useful, giving different opinions on the same subject. It is sometimes worth collecting a range of newspapers for the same day and comparing the articles. This may help you to widen your outlook on a specific topic.

The British Standards Institution

A considerable amount of information and data is available in a series of booklets from the British Standards Institution in London. Information is available on a wide range of topics from engineering and architectural drawing to graphical symbols and anthropometric data (human measurements). Most of the booklets are known by a series of numbers. Ask your teacher if booklets PP7302 and PP7308 are available in school – they may help you with your design work.

Fig. 2.12

Sorting, Interpreting and Analysing Information

When you are using a book to find information, it is not usually necessary to read it from cover to cover – you can dip into it. First of all, use the index to help you to find the relevant section of the book. Then read this through and jot down the main points. If you need to read a large section of a book it is useful to skim through it, jotting down key words, phrases and headings as you find them. It sometimes helps to do this as a spider diagram. You can also dip into or skim through information provided by viewdata and teletext systems.

Remember to write down the titles and authors of the books and other resources that you use, so that they can be listed in the bibliography at the end of your project.

Interpreting information

When using reference material, you will need to be able to interpret tables and graphs. These often give a lot of useful detailed information but you also need to look at the overall picture that they give. Additional information will help you to understand the table or graph better. Fig. 2.13 shows a table comparing life expectancy in 1906 with that in 1986, and Figs. 2.14 and 2.15 give historical facts about the two periods. The table gives the figures and the facts help you to interpret them.

Expectation of life: by sex and age						Fig. 2.13
United Kingdom						Years
	Males			Females		
	1906	1981	1986	1906	1981	1986
Further number of years that a person could expect to live						
At birth	48.0	70.8	71.9	51.6	76.8	77.6
At age						
1 year	55.0	70.7	71.7	57.4	76.6	77.3
10 years	51.4	62.0	62.9	53.9	67.8	68.4
20 years	42.7	52.3	53.1	45.2	57.9	58.6
30 years	34.6	42.7	43.5	36.9	48.1	48.8
40 years	26.8	33.2	34.0	29.1	38.5	39.1
50 years	19.7	24.1	24.9	21.6	29.2	29.8
60 years	13.4	16.3	16.8	14.9	20.8	21.2
70 years	8.4	10.1	10.5	9.2	13.3	13.7
80 years	4.9	5.7	6.0	5.4	7.5	7.8

Facts of life in 1906 — Fig. 2.14

Infant mortality: high.
Life expectancy: a male born in 1906 could expect to live to 48 and a female to 51–52.
Living conditions: poor sanitation.
Diet: limited knowledge about diet so too many foods high in cholesterol eaten.
Medical care: inadequate medicines and high risk of death from an operation.
Main causes of death: tuberculosis, influenza, whooping cough, poliomyelitis, diphtheria, scarlet fever, measles (children) and diseases of the respiratory system.

Facts of life in 1986 — Fig. 2.15

Infant mortality: low.
Life expectancy: a male born in 1986 could expect to live to 71–72 and a female to 77–78.
Living conditions: good sanitation and council housing.
Diet: widespread knowledge about healthy and unhealthy foods.
Medical care: free medical care available to everyone via the National Health Service.
Main causes of death: cancer, heart and circulatory diseases.

In D&T, you will learn to:
use factual information and value judgements
recognise objective and subjective information
collate, sort, analyse, interpret and present information in a form appropriate to the purpose and the intended audience

Analysing information

Once you have collected your information you will need to analyse it. Some of it will be **factual information** as it is based on evidence that is available. This type of information is said to be **objective** as it does not take into account what people think about something. Other information will be **subjective** which means that it is based on people's opinions. People's opinions about things are called **value judgments** and they will vary from one person to another.

It is important to remember the difference between facts and value judgements when you analyse the results of your interviews and questionnaires. You will need to remember that a person's opinions may be based on their situation, surroundings and needs. If you ask many different people their opinions on a particular subject you will receive lots of different answers. For example, people's opinions on children riding their bicycles on the pavement will vary according to their own point of view, as you can see in Fig. 2.16.

Fig. 2.16

Presenting Information

Some of the information that you have collected can be presented graphically – for example, by using **pie charts**, **bar charts** and **pictograms**.

Pie charts

Pie charts are easy to understand and can be very colourful. They are most suitable when you have a complete set of results and you want to show how the individual results compare with one another. To make a pie chart, draw a circle and divide it into sections (the pieces of the pie) according to your results. Each section must be accurately measured and labelled (see Fig. 2.17).

Bar charts

Another graphic presentation is to draw a bar chart like the one shown in Fig. 2.18. Don't forget to label your bar chart down the side and along the bottom.

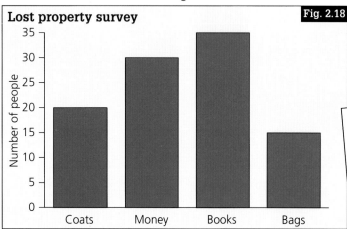

Lost property survey — Fig. 2.18

Pictograms

Pictograms are an attractive way of presenting data. The symbols can be produced very easily by most computers, so you do not have to be good at drawing to use pictograms. Fig. 2.19 gives you an example of a pictogram.

You may be able to use a computer to help you to present your information graphically. Some spreadsheets will produce pie charts and bar charts from the information that you type in.

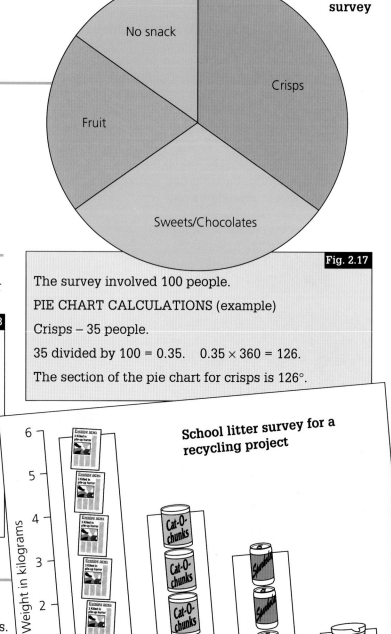

Breaktime snack survey — Fig. 2.17

The survey involved 100 people.

PIE CHART CALCULATIONS (example)

Crisps – 35 people.

35 divided by 100 = 0.35.   0.35 × 360 = 126.

The section of the pie chart for crisps is 126°.

School litter survey for a recycling project — Fig. 2.19

Word processing and desk top publishing

Written notes can be presented neatly and professionally by using a word processor. It allows you to check your work and correct it before printing it out. You can also save the work on a disk and use it again later. **Desk top publishing** is useful because you can often include drawings and, sometimes, even photographs in your work.

Information from CD-ROMs can be loaded into a word processor and used in your investigation. A vast amount of information is available to you in this way. It may not be possible for you to carry out a complete task on a computer screen. If this is the case, word-processed information can be printed out, cut up and stuck on to your work.

Presenting your work

When you have finished your investigations you will probably have a collection of written notes, graphs, charts, drawings, replies to letters, interview notes, completed questionnaires, photographs, tape recordings and, possibly, videotapes. You must then decide how you are going to present this information – for example, in an A3 or A4 folder.

When you are thinking about the layout of the pages try to avoid making the mistake of overcrowding them. Too much information on a page can be difficult for people to take in. However, too little information can be a waste of space. Refer to any photographs or tape recordings you have used and explain why you have chosen that particular method to record the information. Your investigations may lead you to try out some ideas – for example, making prototypes, patterns, plans or trial runs. Don't forget to include these in your presentation.

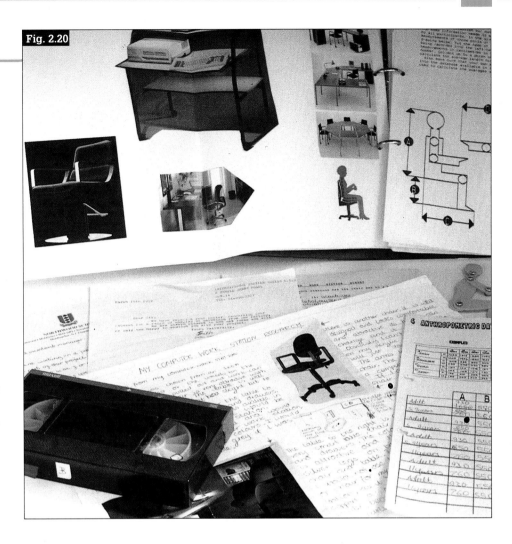

Fig. 2.20

Fig. 2.21

Group presentations

If you are working in a group, you may be asked to present your information to the rest of the group. If it is a small group, you can show them the pages of your folder. If the group is larger, such as the whole class, you will probably need to use an overhead projector. Graphs, charts, drawings and writing can be easily transferred on to thin plastic sheets using a photocopier. These can then be projected on to the wall or a screen using the overhead projector.

You must make sure that everyone in the group can see what you are showing them and hear what you are saying. You should aim to keep your presentation short and to the point.

3 GENERATING A DESIGN

In chapter 1 you read about identifying needs and opportunities for designing. Once you have identified a need, you write a design brief – a simple statement of what product you intend to make to meet the need. The next stage is to write a more detailed statement about your product. This is called the **specification**.

Investigating

In order to write the specification you may need to investigate. It is helpful to examine in detail the need that you are trying to meet. This may mean experiencing a particular problem for yourself. For example, if you are working on a topic which involves people with disabilities, you might find out what it is like to have their particular disability. Have you ever tried using a wheelchair for any length of time, or thought what it must be like not to be able to bend down and pick things up? Experiencing the need at first hand will help your understanding of it.

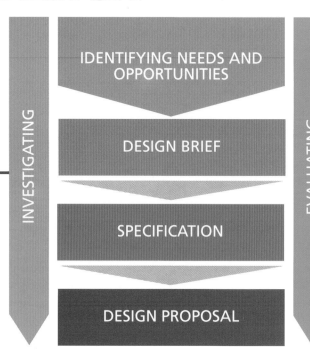

Identifying the constraints

It is important for you to think about all the things that may affect your product, such as how much time and money are available. These things are called **constraints** and they will have an important effect on the outcome of your work. Other constraints will include the materials that are available and your level of ability. It may be necessary for you to learn new skills in order to make your product.

As you think carefully about your task you will be able to identify the constraints that are relevant. These will vary in importance, depending on the nature of the task that you are working on. For example, if you are designing a child's toy, safety will be an important constraint, but if you are working on the design of a leaflet, safety will not be an issue (see Fig. 3.2).

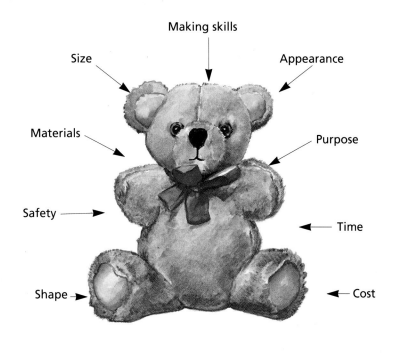

Child's toy

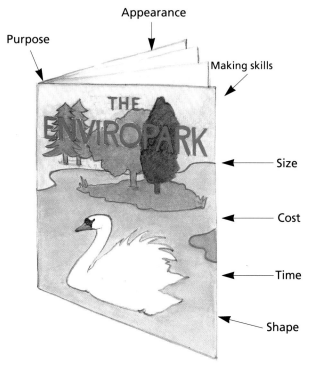

Leaflet

Fig. 3.2

Drawing up a specification

Once you have identified the constraints for your product you can work out the **criteria** that your product needs to meet. For example, one of the constraints for toy products is safety. Therefore, one of the criteria for your toy product for young children is that the product must be safe for that age.

Specification

My toy design for young children should:

- be attractive
- not be too expensive
- be easy for me to make
- be made in the time allowed
- be colourful
- be safe
- be made from the materials available

Fig. 3.3a A simple specification

When you have worked out the criteria that your product should satisfy, you can make a list of them. This forms your specification. You can either write a simple or a more detailed specification. A simple specification lists the criteria in any order of importance. A more detailed specification gives more information, and lists the criteria in two parts – essential criteria and desirable criteria. Essential criteria are the criteria that your product *must* satisfy. Desirable criteria are the criteria that your product *should* satisfy, if possible. Both the simple and the more detailed specifications provide you with a check-list which will help you to evaluate your ideas, your design proposal and the finished product.

Specification

Essential criteria

My toy design for young children must:

1. Be safe for young children to play with. It must have no sharp edges or loose parts.
2. Be attractive and interesting for young children.
3. Be made of wood and plastic.
4. Be made in six weeks.

Desirable criteria

My toy design for young children should:

1. Cost less than £5.00 in materials.
2. Be painted and varnished.
3. Be possible for me to make by myself.

Fig. 3.3b A more detailed specification

Generating a Design Proposal

Once you have drawn up a specification you are ready to start generating a **design proposal**. The aim is to begin with a number of **ideas** (or solutions to a problem) and develop one of these into a design proposal. Fig. 3.4 shows the various stages involved in this.

Ideas

Designers get their ideas from a variety of sources. Leonardo da Vinci is said to have studied the flight of birds when he was designing his flying machines (see Fig. 3.5). Many other designers have been inspired by nature. It is very difficult to think of something that is completely new, so designers sometimes begin by looking at existing products. Many successful designs have been developed from earlier existing designs.

Don't be too worried if you do not feel inspired as you try to think of ideas. The specification will help you because it provides you with a detailed list of the criteria that your finished product should satisfy. Think carefully about each of the criteria in turn and try to keep them in mind as you are working. At this stage you should be trying to produce as many ideas as you can. You should even include the silliest ideas as they may be of use to you later. Ask yourself questions as you work, and try to be as open-minded as possible. You can present your ideas by drawing and modelling them (see pages 32–37).

Although you are advised to produce several ideas, there may be occasions when you can only think of one. Provided that you have given that idea very careful thought and consideration, and you have developed it properly, there is no reason why you should not be able to work from just one idea.

Fig. 3.4

SPECIFICATION

IDEAS

EVALUATING IDEAS

CHOOSING AN IDEA

DESIGN PROPOSAL

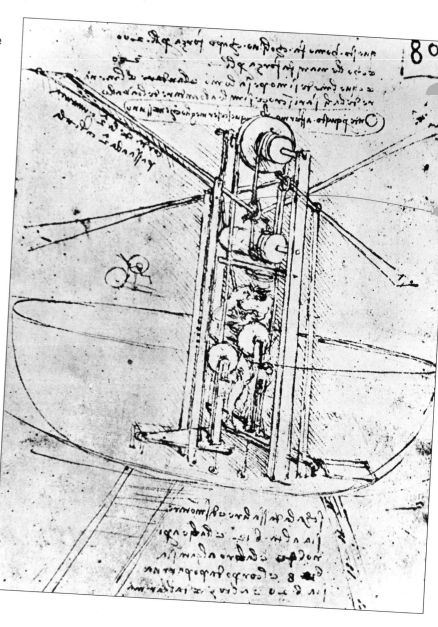

Fig. 3.5 Leonardo da Vinci's sketch for a helicopter design

In D & T, you will learn to:
explore a range of potential solutions before selecting one
maintain a questioning but open-minded approach when developing your ideas
generate ideas and develop them further using a variety of techniques and media
know that the generation of many ideas and the development of single insights can each provide the basis for design proposals
know how designers and technologists have produced ideas and to make use of similar approaches when designing and making

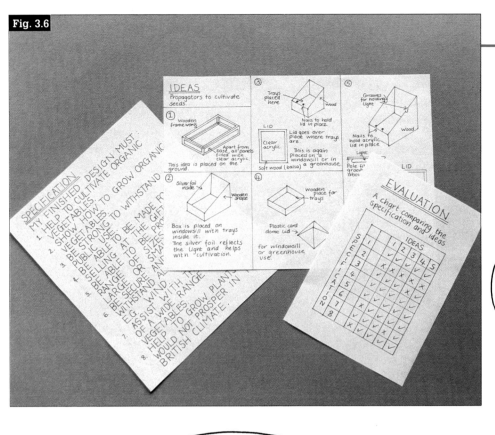

Fig. 3.6

Evaluating ideas

Once you have produced a range of ideas, you can begin the process of choosing the most suitable idea to develop further. This is done by **evaluating** your ideas. Each idea is compared with the specification to see if it will satisfy the specification's criteria. This will help you to see which of your ideas are worth developing further.

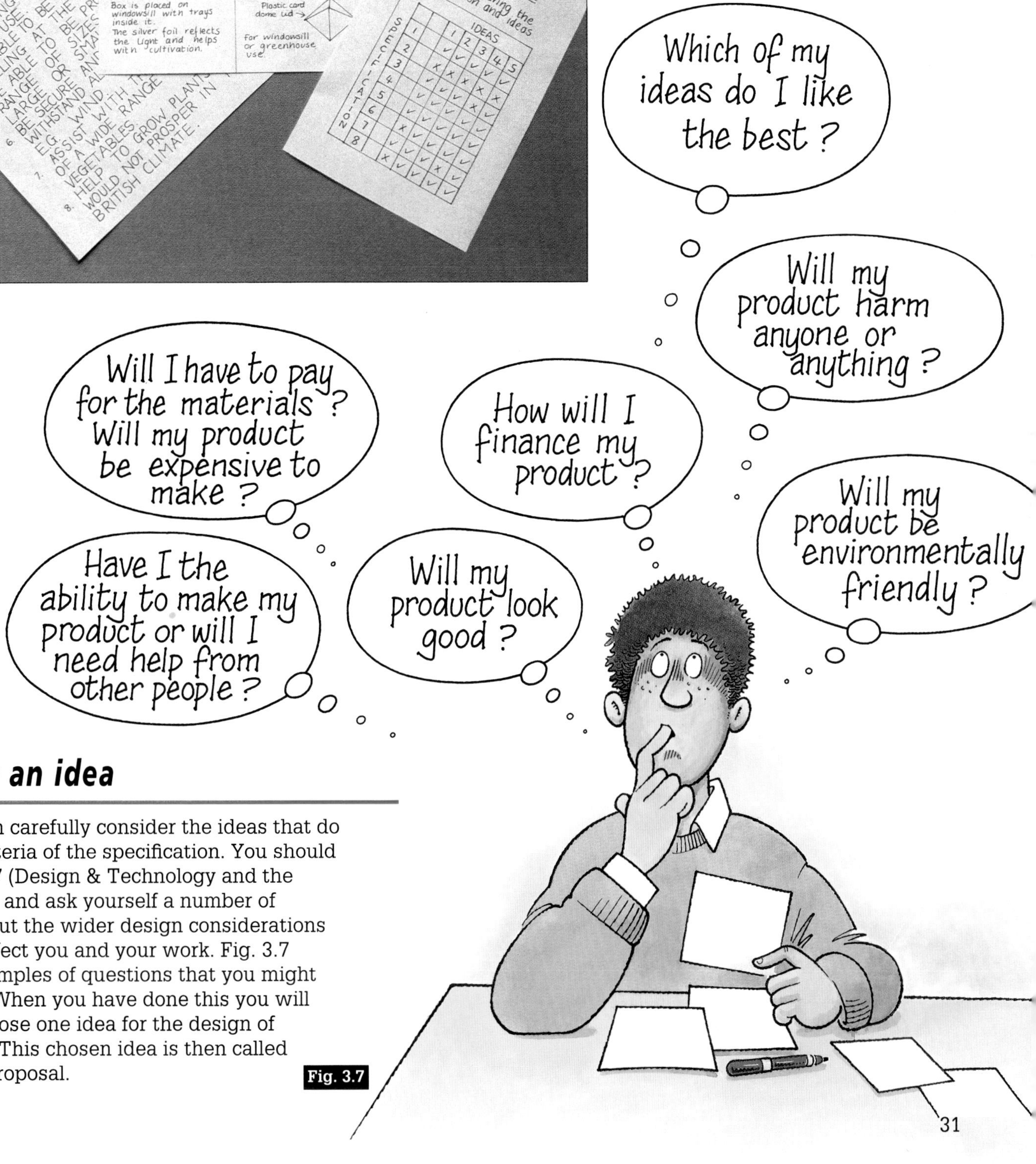

Which of my ideas do I like the best?

Will my product harm anyone or anything?

Will I have to pay for the materials? Will my product be expensive to make?

How will I finance my product?

Will my product be environmentally friendly?

Have I the ability to make my product or will I need help from other people?

Will my product look good?

Choosing an idea

You must then carefully consider the ideas that do satisfy the criteria of the specification. You should read chapter 7 (Design & Technology and the environment), and ask yourself a number of questions about the wider design considerations which may affect you and your work. Fig. 3.7 gives you examples of questions that you might ask yourself. When you have done this you will be able to choose one idea for the design of your product. This chosen idea is then called your design proposal.

Fig. 3.7

Drawing

You can present your design ideas and design proposal by a variety of simple graphic techniques.

Sketching

Sketching is a good way of presenting ideas quickly and freely. Fig. 3.8 shows how a pupil has sketched her ideas for a moving toy. She has used coloured pencils to highlight and render her ideas. Rendering helps to give an impression of what she thinks the finished design might look like.

Sketch lightly and quickly. Don't worry if you go wrong – you can either rub it out or draw over it. Your aim should be to get your ideas down on paper as quickly as you can.

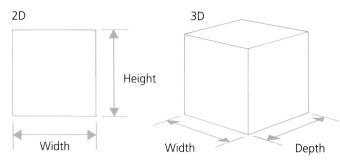

Fig. 3.9a

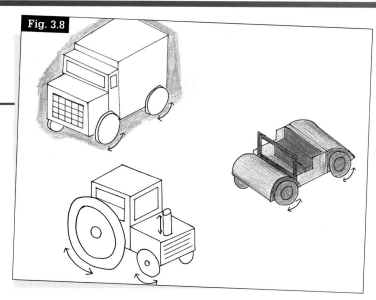

Fig. 3.8

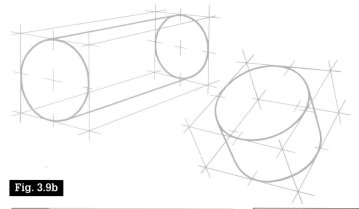

Fig. 3.9b

Sketching in three dimensions

Try to sketch in **three dimensions** (3D) rather than in **two dimensions** (2D) to make your ideas look more solid and realistic (see Fig. 3.9a). Draw curved or round objects inside boxes (crates). This is called **crating** and it will help you to draw complicated shapes more easily (see Fig. 3.9b). There are various methods of drawing objects. Fig. 3.9c shows two of them – oblique and isometric drawing.

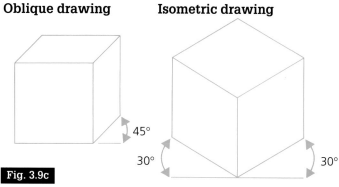

Fig. 3.9c

In D & T, you will learn to:
take account of human scale and proportion when designing
develop a range of simple skills used in drawing and modelling
use specialist vocabulary when communicating proposals
develop styles of visual communication which take account of what is to be conveyed, the audience and the medium to be used
recognise the relationships between two-dimensional representation and three-dimensional forms

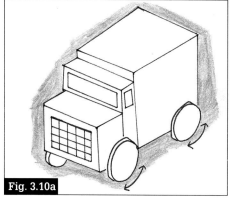

Fig. 3.10a

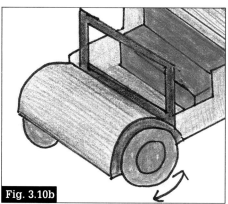

Fig. 3.10b

Highlighting and rendering

It is helpful to **highlight** your best ideas by drawing round them with coloured pencils or felt-tipped pens (see Fig. 3.10a). This will make them stand out on the page. You can also use coloured pencils and pens to show the materials that you are likely to use. This is called **rendering** (see Fig. 3.10b).

Flow charts

Ideas for the design of a system may at first appear to be more difficult to draw. However, a **flow chart** can be used to show how a system works. Fig. 3.11 shows a flow chart for the system in a supermarket. For more examples of flow charts, see Fig. 1.15 on page 16 and Fig. 4.28 on page 48. A flow chart is also an example of two-dimensional modelling. (For more information on this see page 34).

Perspective drawing

Some environments can be drawn using **perspective drawing**. Architects sometimes use very accurate and carefully drawn perspective drawings to show what a new building will look like, and to give some idea of how it will fit in with its environment. Fig. 3.12 shows a **single-point perspective** drawing of a kitchen and Fig. 3.13 shows a **two-point perspective** drawing of a kitchen. Drawings like this are made when designing and planning a new kitchen. They give a good idea of what the environment of the room will be like. A perspective drawing is another example of two-dimensional modelling (see page 34).

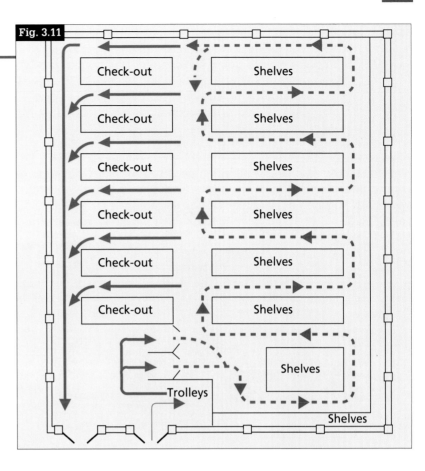

Fig. 3.11

Fig. 3.12 A single-point perspective drawing

Fig. 3.13 A two-point perspective drawing

EXTRAS

1. Draw a flow chart to show the movement of people working in a kitchen.

2. Make a perspective drawing to show a particular environment in or around your school, for example a classroom.

Modelling

Making a **model** of a design idea or a design proposal can be one of the most exciting stages of the design process. You may use modelling to develop your design proposal before going on to make the finished product. However, there will be times when it will be impossible to make the finished product, so you will make a presentation model instead. There are two forms of modelling – **two-dimensional** and **three-dimensional**.

Two-dimensional modelling

Two-dimensional modelling is often used to represent a system or an environment. For example, the operations of a system can be shown by a flow chart, and an environment can be shown by a perspective drawing (see page 33). A computer can also be used to make two-dimensional models (see pages 36–37).

Fig. 3.14

Fig. 3.15

Fig. 3.16

	In D & T, you will learn to:
	make two- or three-dimensional models of your design ideas and to test these before proceeding further
	extend the range of techniques used in your drawing and modelling
	present your design and technological ideas and proposals using modelling techniques and specialist vocabulary
	distinguish between various techniques of modelling and use appropriate techniques for developing proposals

Three-dimensional modelling

Three-dimensional modelling is an excellent way of testing your design ideas to find out if they will work. This is particularly important when you are working on a mechanical topic involving moving parts. Simple models can be quickly constructed using modelling kits such as Lego or Fisher Tecnic. Materials, such as card, thin plastic or plasticine, are useful for three-dimensional modelling. It is a good idea to record your model by drawing a sketch of it, or taking a photograph of it. The skills and techniques needed to make three-dimensional models are covered in detail in *Techniques and Resources* (the other Design & Technology book in this series).

Presentation models

In school, a presentation model is made when it is impossible to make the actual product. It shows as clearly as possible what the finished product would look like. The model can be an artefact, a system or an environment. You may need to make a presentation model if you are working on an industry-based project such as redesigning an existing product.

Fig. 3.17

Fig. 3.18

Architects use presentation models to present design proposals to clients. This type of model is often a block model made from wood, styrofoam or plaster. Fig. 3.19 shows an architect's model.

Fig. 3.19

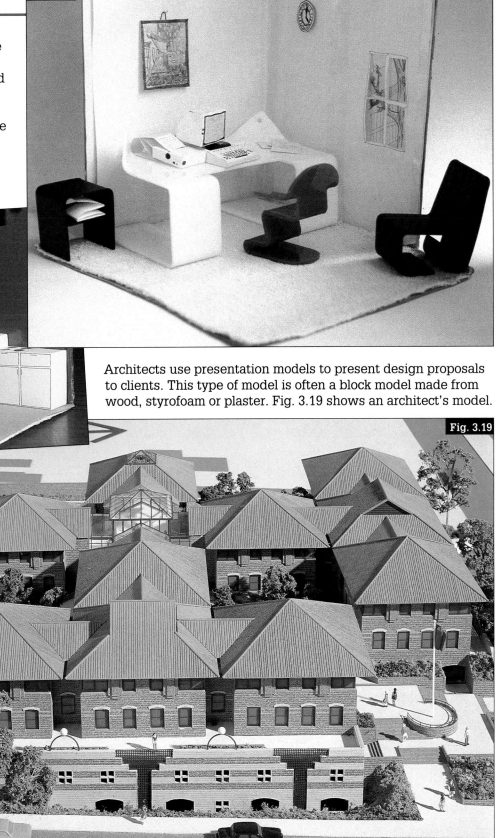

Using the Computer

A computer can be very useful for helping you to present your design ideas and design proposal.

Desk top publishing

Desk top publishing (DTP) software allows you to include graphics, drawings and, in some cases, photographs with your text. You can make the drawings yourself using a graphics program or you can use drawings which are already available on a disc. Collections of drawings called clip art are available on disc for use on a computer.

Computer-aided design

Designing on a computer screen is known as **computer-aided design** (CAD). It is an example of two-dimensional modelling. It is possible to use the computer in a variety of ways from simple drawing programs to complicated CAD systems. Fig. 3.20 shows an electronic circuit that has been modelled using a computer software package. Fig. 3.21 shows how a fitted kitchen has been designed on a computer and the design printed out for the customer. It is possible to design like this yourself using a computer software package called TechSoft Designer.

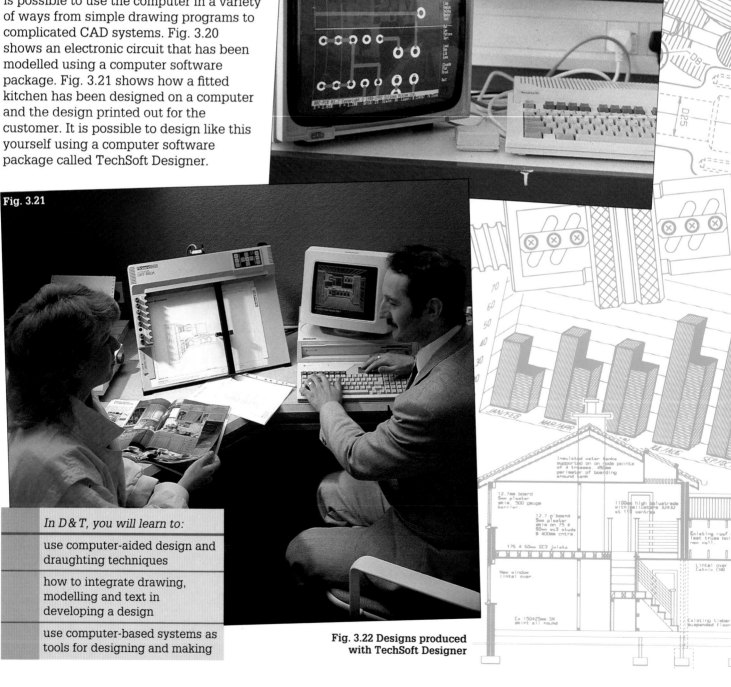

Fig. 3.20

Fig. 3.21

In D&T, you will learn to:

use computer-aided design and draughting techniques

how to integrate drawing, modelling and text in developing a design

use computer-based systems as tools for designing and making

Fig. 3.22 Designs produced with TechSoft Designer

Computer-aided manufacture

Computers can be used to control machines during the making process. They have been used to do this in industry for many years. This process is known as **computer-aided manufacture** (CAM).

CAD/CAM

When computer-aided design work is produced by computer-controlled machines, the process is called CAD/CAM. The Roland CAMM-1 desktop sign maker (see Fig. 3.23) allows CAD/CAM to be carried out very simply in schools. A design drawn on a CAD system can be printed out using a pen on paper, or it can be cut out of card or coloured vinyl by using a carbide-tipped cutter. This provides an excellent way of making cardboard models, signs, and even patterns for fabrics.

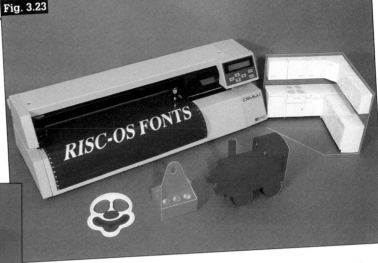
Fig. 3.23

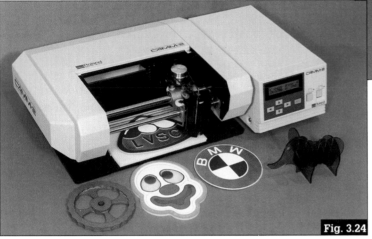
Fig. 3.24

The Roland CAMM-2 computer-aided engraving machine (see Fig. 3.24) works in a similar way. A design drawn on a CAD system can be engraved on acrylic, metal or glass. The design can also be cut out of various materials very accurately. The machine is useful for making jewellery, acrylic signs and almost anything else which requires very accurate cutting out.

Computer numerical control

The engineering industry uses a type of computer-aided manufacture known as **computer numerical control** (CNC). Programs made up of a series of numbers are used to control and operate the machines. It may be possible for you to use CNC in your work. Computer programs such as TechSoft CNC Designer allow you to design an object on the screen and then make it using computer-controlled machines. Fig 3.25 shows the stages involved in making a product using CAD/CAM and CNC lathe.

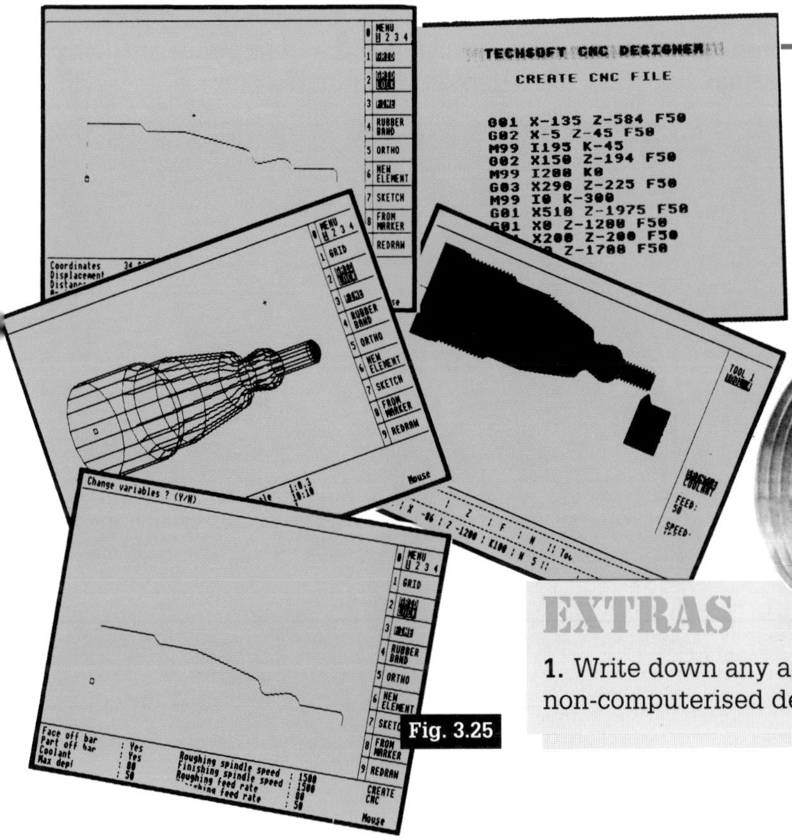

Fig. 3.25

EXTRAS

1. Write down any advantages that you think CAD/CAM may have over non-computerised design and making techniques.

4 PLANNING

Planning is a very important part of the design process. Careful planning will enable you to turn your ideas into reality (realisation). Planning your project thoroughly will help to prevent you from making mistakes and wasting both materials and time.

You will need to work out certain details of your chosen design – for example, how big it will be, what sort of materials and equipment you will need and what will be the best way of producing it. You will have to find out how much time you have available for the project and then plan your work within the time allowed.

Fig. 4.1 Planning a project

Planning your project enables you to organise the making of your product. Here are some simple questions that you can ask yourself in order to help you with your planning:

● Do you have all the skills needed to make the product that you have designed or will you need to ask your teacher for help?

● Have you used all the materials before or do you need help from a teacher who is a specialist in another area of technology?

Planning in industry

Planning is important in schoolwork when you are working with different materials and specialist equipment, but it is even more important in the manufacturing industry. Industrial products are not usually made entirely by one person – the individual parts are made by many different people. Parts are often made in factories in different parts of the country and, sometimes, even in different parts of the world.

It is, therefore, essential that the work is carefully planned so that the parts can be brought together for the finished product to be assembled successfully.

Fig. 4.2 shows Sony televisions being assembled. Each television consists of components and parts from many different places, made by many different people.

Fig. 4.2

In D&T, you will learn to:
analyse the task and its components, to identify those which depend upon the completion of previous tasks, and to develop a flow chart
set objectives and identify resources and constraints
organise your work, taking account of constraints

Planning can be divided into three main areas: **product planning, resource planning** and **action planning**. These are explained briefly on this page and explored in more detail in the rest of the chapter.

Product planning

Working drawings are used to plan and organise the making of a product. They enable you to think about the size of the parts of the product and the way in which they will be fitted together.

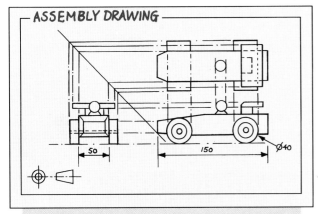

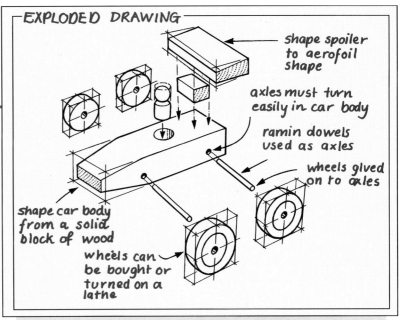

▲ **Fig. 4.3 Examples of working drawings**

Resource planning

It is important to work out exactly what materials and parts are required to make your product. It is, therefore, useful to make a list of the resources you will need. This will also show you which materials and parts you will have to order. The list can be used to work out the material cost of your product.

Fig 4.5 A flow chart for making cheese and tomato on toast

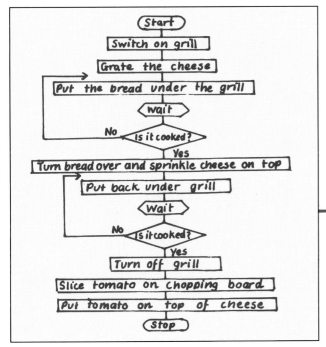

TOY PROJECT: PARTS LIST			
Part	Material	Size(mm)	No.of
body	beech	150x50x30	1
wheels	beech	Ø40x15	4
axles	dowel	Ø6x80	2
driver	beech	Ø15x30	1
spoiler	beech	70x30x10	1
support	beech	30x20x15	1

▲ ◀ **Fig. 4.4 Examples of resource planning**

Action planning

Before you start to make anything, it is important to work out the best way of going about it. Which part do you need to make first? You may need to wait for glue or paint to dry before you can continue. Have you considered this? When working with food, or preparing meals, you will need to plan your work so that the various dishes are ready at the right time. Flow charts, sequential drawings and time plans are used to help you to plan the making of your product.

Product Planning – Working Drawings

Once you have formed your design proposal you will need to think very carefully about how you are going to make your design. You must make a number of decisions about the product – for example, how big it will be, what materials and equipment will be used to make it, how it will be made and what sort of finish it will have. The models and drawings of your design proposal can be used to help you to make these decisions. This information can then be translated into drawings called **working drawings**. These show all the information needed for someone to be able to make a product. You need to remember that, in industry, the person who designs a product is not always the person who will make it.

One working drawing can be very different from another. Drawings vary according to the sort of product being made and the materials used to make it. A product made of a construction material, such as plastic or metal, will have a different type of drawing from a product made of fabric. A food product may hardly need any drawings at all but it will need accurate planning in other ways. In most cases, a working drawing will consist of a very careful and accurate drawing of the product you intend to make. It will include all the information needed for you to make your product.

Fig. 4.6 A polystyrene model is used to help plan the making of a product

Fig. 4.7 Different examples of working drawings

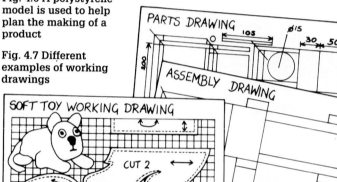

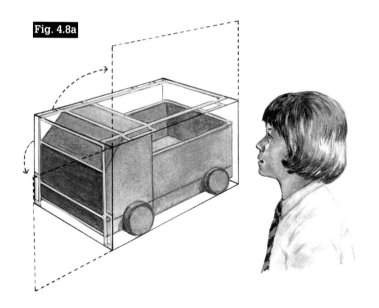

Fig. 4.8a

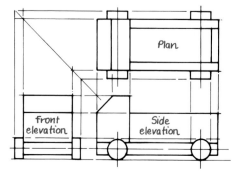

Fig. 4.8b

Orthographic projection

Many designers use a system of drawing called **orthographic projection**. Drawings done in this way show the product from different angles so that every detail of the design is shown.

Two types of orthographic projection can be used : **first angle projection** and **third angle projection**. First angle projection can be more difficult to understand so it is simpler to use third angle projection for your working drawings.

Third angle projection

To understand the layout of third angle projection drawings you have to imagine that the object to be drawn is inside a glass box. The view of the object as seen from one angle is then projected on to the glass as shown in Fig. 4.8a. If you imagine unfolding the box in the direction of the arrows, it would look like the drawing in Fig. 4.8b. This shows the side elevation, the front elevation and the plan view of the object.

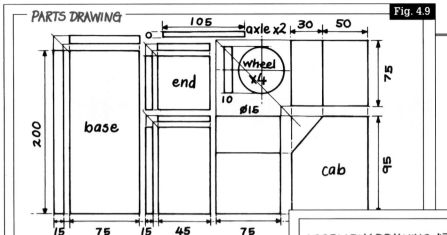

PARTS DRAWING

Fig. 4.9

Parts drawings

If a product consists of several different parts, it may be a good idea to make a **parts drawing**. Each part is drawn in orthographic projection, clearly showing its size. The parts drawing contains enough information for each individual part to be made. Fig. 4.9 shows the parts drawing for a wooden lorry, designed for a child's toy project.

Assembly drawings

In order to show how the component parts fit together, an **assembly drawing** is made. This shows the final assembled product with all its parts in place. Like the parts drawing, it is drawn using orthographic projection showing three views of the product. Assembly drawings provide enough information for someone to assemble the product.

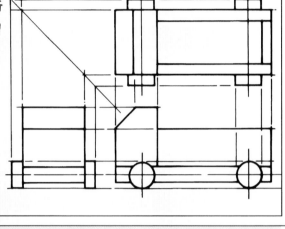

ASSEMBLY DRAWING

All parts are sanded and finished with clear polyurethane varnish. They are glued together with PVA.

Fig. 4.10

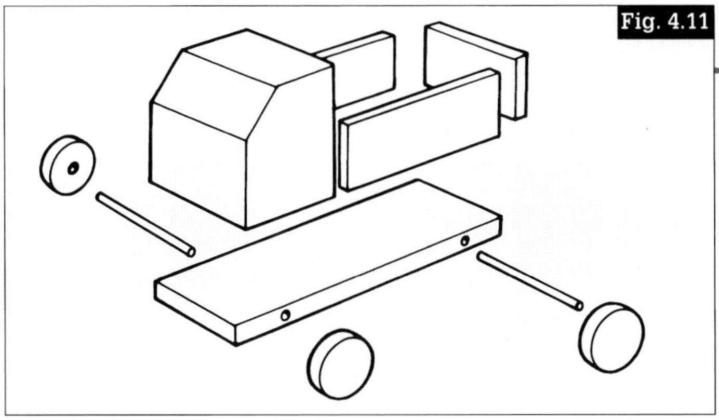

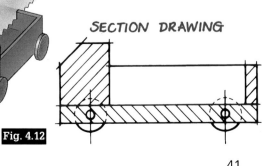

Fig. 4.11

Exploded drawings

Another way of showing how a product is assembled is to use an **exploded drawing**. If you look in car or motorcycle repair manuals, you will find many examples of exploded drawings. Instructions for objects which you have to put together yourself, such as furniture, often use this type of drawing.

Exploded drawings can be very useful when you want to show how something is assembled. They will help you to plan the making of your product.

Sections

Sometimes it is necessary to show what an object looks like inside, in order to understand how it is made. Dotted or broken lines are sometimes used on drawings to show things which you cannot see. Drawings can become very confusing if too many dotted lines are used so it is often better to make a **section drawing** of the object instead.

A section drawing shows an object which has been 'cut' to show what is happening inside. The parts which have actually been cut through are shown by diagonal lines drawn on them. These lines are known as hatching.

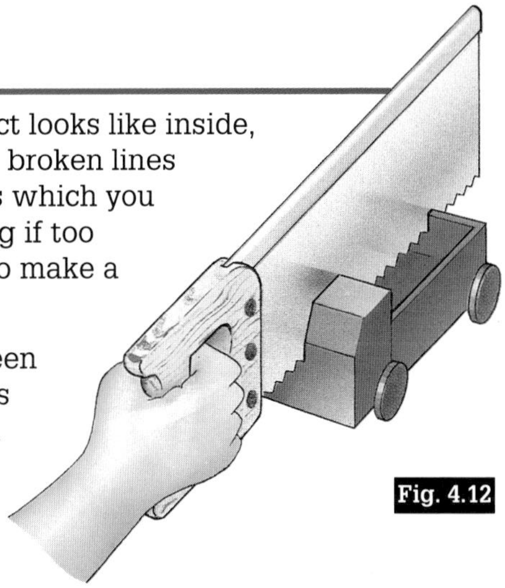

SECTION DRAWING

Fig. 4.12

Product Planning – Food and Fabric

If you have decided to work with food in your project work, working drawings may not be relevant for the planning process. Drawings may be unnecessary but notes and sketches can be used to record your plans instead. Writing down your plans will help you to see what tasks need to be done. You can then put the tasks in order of importance which will help you to think about the most important things first.

Asking questions

Asking yourself questions is another way to begin planning. The answers will form the basis of your plan. Try asking yourself these questions next time you work with food.

● Can I make it? Is my project suitable for my level of ability – not too easy but not too hard ?

● Do I have all the skills I need or will my teacher have to help me?

● Do I need any special equipment, such as a food processor, a microwave oven, scientific equipment for experimental work or a computer to analyse nutrients?

● What ingredients will I need? How much will they cost? Can I use a database to find out the cost?

● Will I need any special dishes to serve my food in or containers to take it home in?

Fig. 4.13

Fig. 4.14

You can also ask yourself these questions to help you plan when you are working with fabric.

● Will I need any patterns or templates? How much will they cost?

● What colour combinations will be suitable for my product?

When choosing or making patterns for clothes, it is important to ask yourself if the style is suitable and the pattern the right size for you. Choosing fabric for clothes raises many more questions which need to be answered.

● Are the design and texture of the fabric suitable for the style?

● Does the fabric have a one-way design, like tartan (see Fig. 4.14)? Does it have a 'nap' which means that the fibres 'stroke' one way, like velvet?

In D&T, you will learn to:

set objectives and identify resources and constraints

Patterns and templates

Plastic, wood, metal, fabric and some foods are materials which are often used in sheet form in Design & Technology. **Patterns** and **templates** are used to transfer the shape of the design from your drawings on to the sheet material. They are useful because they can help you to find out how much material is needed. This will allow you to use the material in the most economic way, keeping waste to a minimum.

Top: Fig. 4.16 Basic geometric shapes for clothes

Left: Fig. 4.17 Basic designs for a shirt

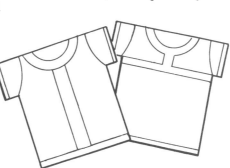

Patterns

When working with fabric, you will usually be expected to design and make your own pattern, but sometimes it will be possible to use a ready-made one. You can make your own pattern using squared drafting paper. Fig. 4.16 shows that geometric shapes can be used to make excellent basic clothes. Fig. 4.17 shows how a basic design for a top or shirt can be adapted in different ways with a little imagination. The pattern pieces needed for the design can be drawn on to squared drafting paper, cut out and pinned to the fabric.

There are several points to consider when making your own patterns:

● You must take careful and accurate measurements. It is a good idea to ask your teacher or a friend to help you do this.

● You must remember to allow enough material for movement when making clothes.

● You will also need to allow extra fabric for the seams.

● Write special instructions on each pattern piece – for example, how many pieces need to be cut out.

● When pinning the pattern pieces on to the fabric you must take into account the design, nap and grain of the fabric.

Computer programs, FADS for example, can be used to help you to design clothes. You could find out from your teacher if this software is available in your school.

Templates

Patterns are used in other areas of Design & Technology but then they are usually called templates. When working with acrylic, you have probably made a template from card and then drawn around it on the acrylic with a chinagraph pencil or a marker pen.

Fig. 4.18 A card template being used to trace a shape on acrylic

When working with food, special cutters are used to cut shapes out of pastry, marzipan and biscuit mixture. These are really templates made of metal or plastic. Fig. 4.20 shows some of the cutters used to make the gingerbread biscuits shown in Fig. 4.21.

Fig. 4.19 A template used for patchwork

Fig. 4.20 Examples of cutters used to make gingerbread biscuits

Fig. 4.21

EXTRAS

1. Write down the recipe for a savoury dish that you like. Then use a computer program or food tables to analyse the nutrients of your dish. Do they meet the Recommended Daily Amount (RDA) of nutrients for an 11-13 year old? If not, suggest how these missing nutrients can be supplied at other meals in the day.

2. Study the instructions on a pattern instruction sheet. Then write down a set of pattern instructions for a design that you have chosen to make.

Resource Planning

Before you can begin to make your chosen design, it is important that you make a list of everything you will need. This is not difficult if you have made a working drawing of your product or a detailed plan of what you are going to do.

The type of list you make will vary according to the project that you are doing. You will be able to use it to find out the material cost of your finished product. You can use either price lists or a computer database to work this out.

Parts lists

Fig. 4.22 shows the **parts list** for the toy racing car shown on page 39. From the list, it is possible to work out exactly how much material is needed and which parts, if any, can be bought ready-made.

Similar lists can be made when working with fabric. The pattern pieces can be used to find out how much fabric will be needed.

Fig. 4.22

No.	Part	Material	Size	No.of
1.	body	beech	150x50x30	1
2.	wheels	beech	Ø40x15	4
3.	axles	dowel	Ø6 x80	2
4.	driver	beech	Ø15x30	1
5.	spoiler	beech	70x30x10	1
6.	support	beech	30x20x15	1

Fig. 4.23

Ingredients list	Equipment required
white cabbage	sharp knife
carrots	cutting board
tomatoes	saucers
celery	large bowl
cucumber	metal spoon
red or green peppers	pair of scissors
apples	
lemon juice	
sultanas	
bacon	

Ingredients lists

Projects involving the use of food require **ingredients lists**, but it is a good idea to include the equipment needed as well so that everything is to hand when you are ready to start work. Fig. 4.23 shows a list of ingredients and equipment needed for a winter salad.

Components lists

Projects which involve electronics will require a **components list**. Many of the items required may be available in your school but you may need specialised components which will have to be ordered.

There may be times when you will not be able to obtain an item you require for your design work. If this happens, you will have to use an alternative part or modify your plans.

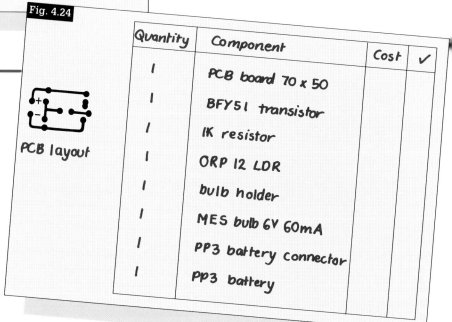

Fig. 4.24

PCB layout

Quantity	Component	Cost	✓
1	PCB board 70 x 50		
1	BFY51 transistor		
1	1K resistor		
1	ORP 12 LDR		
1	bulb holder		
1	MES bulb 6V 60mA		
1	PP3 battery connector		
1	PP3 battery		

In D&T, you will learn to:	
produce a documented plan for your work, including an analysis of the resources required and a time schedule	
modify a plan, as necessary, explaining the need for changes	

Have you forgotten anything?

Check your lists carefully. Is there anything you may have forgotten? It is often a good idea to get a friend to check your list for you. Don't forget to include parts like hinges, handles and other fittings in your parts list. You may have to obtain these yourself.

If you are working with fabric, you will probably need items like buttons, zips or elastic. These are known as 'notions' and you may have to make a separate list for them.

Specialist items of equipment are sometimes needed in order to carry out certain tasks. You will need to know who to ask to help you to obtain these items. Try to remember that you are the designer and it is up to you to organise your resources. Other people will help you but you cannot expect them to do it for you.

Organising your resources

You will need to look carefully at your lists and find out what is available in school and what needs to be obtained elsewhere. Is there anything that you can bring in from home?

Look at the ingredients list shown in Fig. 4.23. Where can you find the ingredients required?

Ask yourself the following questions:

● Can you order them from school?

● Can you bring them from home? (Remember to ask in plenty of time before the lesson.)

● Are some of the ingredients in the freezer?

● Which fresh ingredients will you need to buy the day before the lesson?

● How much will it cost?

Copy out the list of ingredients and tick those you can order from school or bring in from home. Make a list of the items that you are left with, and write down where you would buy them.

You may need to obtain a particular type of fabric for your design work. Do you know where to buy it and how it is sold? Fabric is available on rolls in different widths: 90 cm (36"), 115 cm (45") and 150 cm (60") and is bought by length. It is also possible to buy remnants from shops and market stalls. These are

Fig. 4.25 A selection of fabrics

Fig. 4.26 Construction materials on display in a DIY store

ready-cut pieces labelled with the length and width. They are usually good value for money.

If you are working with construction materials you may find DIY stores useful. Most larger stores have a good range of fixtures and fittings as well as materials on display. Some stores give away catalogues. These are worth collecting as a resource to help you with your work.

EXTRAS

1. Use a computer database or electronics catalogue to find out the cost of the items shown on the components list in Fig. 4.24.

2. Use the Yellow Pages to find out where your nearest DIY store is situated. Arrange to visit it to find out what it stocks.

Action Planning

To make sure that you make the best use of your time, energy and resources, it is important to make a plan of action that you can follow during the making process.

Before starting to make your product, you must plan what you are going to do. It is important to remember that some tasks must be completed before others can be started. For example, a product may need to be varnished or painted before it is finally put together. If you are making a meal, it is important that all the dishes are ready at exactly the right time. Some food spoils if it has to be kept hot for any length of time before serving.

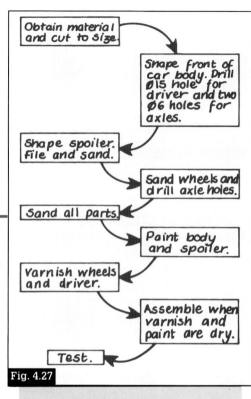

Fig. 4.27

Block diagrams

Action planning requires you to be logical, as you must work out exactly what needs to be done and in what order. The simplest way to plan is to make a **block diagram** as follows. Write down all the tasks that need to be done and put them into the correct order. Then draw a box around each task that you have

identified. You may be able to group related tasks together in one box. The boxes show the stages of the making process. Link the boxes together with arrows to show the order of the stages. Fig. 4.27 shows a block diagram of the stages involved in making the toy racing car.

Flow charts

The stages involved in making something can be shown on a **flow chart** like the one shown in Fig. 4.28. A number of different symbols are used to show the various types of action involved in the making process. The British Standards Institution has recommended a list of symbols so that everyone can recognise them. They are shown in Fig. 4.29.

Fig. 4.28

Start
Switch on grill
Grate the cheese
Put the bread under the grill
wait
No — Is it cooked?
Yes
Turn bread over and sprinkle cheese on top
Put back under grill
wait
No — Is it cooked?
Yes
Turn off grill
Slice tomato on chopping board
Put tomato on top of cheese
Stop

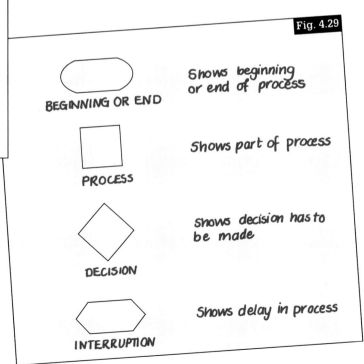

In D&T, you will learn to:
organise your working to complete the task on time
estimate how long an activity might take, and the resources required, and take this into account in your planning
estimate the time taken, and the resources required, to complete the task and its components

Sequential diagrams

Sequential diagrams or step-by-step instructions are drawings used to show how to make something. You have probably made a model kit which had a set of instructions consisting mainly of drawings. Flat pack, self-assembly furniture uses instructions like this to show you how to put it together. Commercial sewing patterns usually contain a making-up sheet and patterns found in books and magazines also give step-by-step instructions, using drawings or photographs. Can you think of any other things that have step-by-step instructions? Fig. 4.30 shows a making-up sheet and step-by-step instructions.

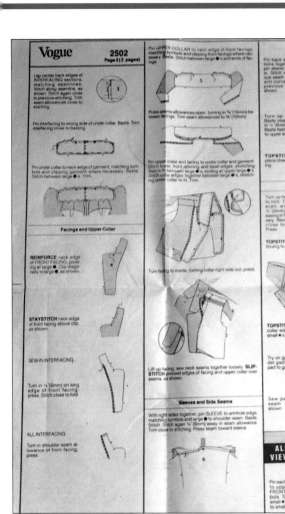

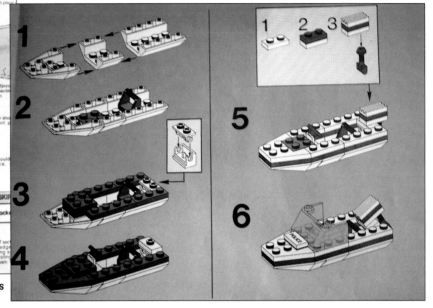

Fig. 4.30 A making-up sheet and step-by-step instructions

Time planning

Some projects may take several weeks to complete and you will need to plan ahead. You will need to estimate how long you think it will take to complete each part of the process. A **work plan** for the whole term may be needed. This can be set out like the one shown in Fig. 4.31. You may need to change or improve this to suit your own work. If your plan shows what you intend to do in one particular lesson, then it could look something like the **time plan** shown in Fig. 4.32. It shows the work needed to complete the task, the resources and equipment required, and the time allowed to do the work.

PEANUT BUTTER COOKIES

Ingredients	Time	Order of work	Special points
50g SR flour pinch of salt	0915	Sift together flour, salt and semolina.	
50g peanut butter few drops of vanilla essence	0920	Cream fat, sugar, peanut butter and vanilla essence together until light.	Measure essence with teaspoon.
25g semolina 50g butter/margarine 50g soft brown sugar 1 egg	0925	Beat in egg, then stir in dry ingredients.	Switch oven on to gas mark 4, 180°C.
	0930	Drop teaspoons of mixture on to ungreased baking tray. Bake for 10-12 mins.	
	0940	Wash up. Remove cookies from oven. Cool on wire tray.	Switch oven off.

WORK PLAN

Week	Task	Equipment required	Work completed
1			
2			
3			
4			
5			
6			

Left: Fig. 4.31
A work plan

Above: Fig. 4.32
A time plan

EXTRAS

1. In a group, have a brainstorming session about a meal for a special occasion. Make the necessary plans between you, sharing out the time, the cost and the different jobs to be done.

5 MAKING

After you have planned your Design & Technology project work you are ready to turn your ideas into reality (realisation). This is the making stage. For many people, this is the most enjoyable and exciting part of Design & Technology. This chapter provides you with an introduction to making. *Techniques and Resources* (the other Design & Technology book in this series) will help you work with the different materials and techniques you will use during the making stage.

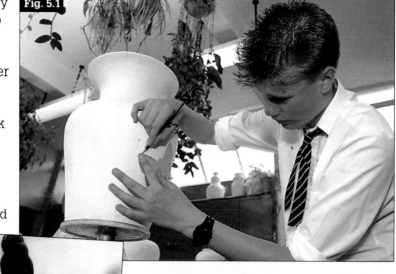

Fig. 5.1

You will be involved in a variety of different making activities in your Design & Technology lessons. The materials you will work with will range from food and textiles to resistant materials, such as metal or plastic. You might be working with materials to produce an artefact, such as a meal or a model of an environment such as a railway station. When you are designing a system you might not be involved in actually making a product. Instead, your outcome could be a flow chart showing, for example, a system for traffic flow. The form your making activity takes will depend on the design proposal that you have produced.

	In D&T, you will learn to:
	aim for a high quality of accuracy and presentation
	select a match of materials and equipment to create a quality outcome
	understand that it may be necessary to practise an operation in order to improve the quality

Aim for quality

Always aim to produce work of the highest quality. Remember, that what you make might last a long time. Be as accurate as you can when working with materials and present your work as neatly as you can. Select and match materials that will help you to create a quality piece of work. If you are not happy with your skill in a particular technique, practise it before using it in your project work.

Be prepared

In most cases making will not be too difficult. If you have thought carefully about what you are going to make, and planned and prepared properly, then the making should be very straightforward.

Fig. 5.2

Fig. 5.3

Ask for help and advice

You may need to ask for help with techniques and materials that are new to you. Your teacher will be available for help so don't forget to ask. Sometimes they may not know all the answers themselves and they may send you to an expert. Remember that your teachers have different specialist skills. Many are experts in a particular area and it is important for you to use their strengths where you can.

Work safely

Safety is very important when working with tools, materials and equipment, as it is at this stage when accidents are most likely to happen. Always try to be aware of the dangers when using practical areas, and work as safely as possible. Keep the area around you clean and tidy, and put things away when you have finished with them. Never run in workshops or practical rooms, and always take great care when handling sharp tools or hot materials. Protect yourself by wearing suitable protective clothing, and always follow safety precautions.

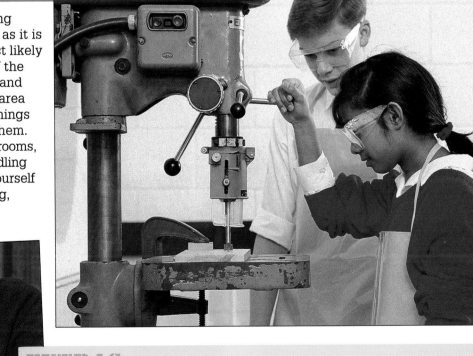
Fig. 5.4a

Fig. 5.4b

EXTRAS

1. Think about the accidents that could occur when you are working in practical areas. Make a list of what you could do to prevent these accidents from happening.

Fig. 5.5

Make the most of your team

Working in a team or a group can be a very enjoyable way of working, provided that everyone knows what they have to do and does their share. Important decisions should be made together and the making tasks shared out as fairly as possible. If you are leading a team, don't be tempted to keep the best jobs for yourself and give the boring ones away. Try to give the tasks to the people who you think will be most able to carry them out. If someone is good at something, you should try to make use of their skill. For example, if you are working in a group to prepare a children's party, the person with the neatest handwriting could be responsible for writing the invitations and the name cards. Another person, who has a talent for making cakes, could cook some fairy cakes; someone else in your group, who makes delicious pastry, could make the sausage rolls; and an artistic person could be responsible for icing and decorating the birthday cake. But remember to share out the clearing up fairly. When working in a team or a group always make sure that you know what you have to do. If you are in any doubt, consult the other members or ask your teacher.

Make notes on your project

Make notes about your project as your work progresses. You should include information about any problems that you have and how you solve them, and any changes that you make to your original design. You may want to take photographs or video your work at various stages of the making process. This information can be used when you write your final evaluation. (See pages 54–55 for more details.)

Fig. 5.6

In D & T, you will learn to:
realise that, when working in teams, people may have specialist roles
allocate tasks when leading a team

Ailuropoda melanoleuca

Learn from your experience

As you progress through your Design & Technology course you will gain experience in designing and making. It is important that you use your knowledge to help you when you are working with, or choosing, materials and equipment. Try to learn to trust your own judgement and make decisions for yourself. Don't worry if you make a few mistakes at first, as learning from your own experience is a very valuable exercise. You may want to answer a question yourself and then check with your teacher to make sure that your answer is correct. You may be surprised to see just how quickly you will gain the confidence to make decisions for yourself.

Fig. 5.7

Look at other books

Techniques and Resources (the other Design & Technology book in this series) contains information about the materials that you are likely to be using and has details of how to work with them. Look at the book before you start your making activity to check that you know what you need to do.

You may want to refer to it again at various stages of the making process, or if you are unsure about anything. It will also help you if you have a problem and your teacher is not able to help you immediately. Don't waste valuable time waiting – check with the book first.

Fig. 5.8

EXTRAS

1. Imagine that you are working in a group to design a nursery. Make a list of the different tasks that will have to be shared out. Beside each task write down the skills needed to do that particular task.

6 EVALUATING

Evaluating is a natural part of designing for most people. It is unusual for a person to make something without considering how successful it is, or how difficult it was to produce. Only a few people are completely satisfied with their work. Most people, if they are being honest with themselves, will be able to suggest improvements that they could make. You may even evaluate your work without realising – when you reject some of your first ideas, for example. This will certainly happen as you become more experienced in designing and making.

Evaluating is very important in business and in industry. Companies evaluate how they make things so that they produce goods as efficiently as possible. Consumers are sometimes asked to evaluate products and services so that companies can find out the consumers' needs. Many products that appear to be new on the market are the result of industrial designers redesigning and changing existing ones.

Fig. 6.1 An industrial product being evaluated

Evaluation as a starting point

In school you may be asked to evaluate existing products and then improve or redesign them. This is using evaluating as a starting point (see pages 60–61).

Final evaluation

When you have completed your Design & Technology project you will be asked to write a final evaluation. This means that you have to assess the success of your design work. Did you fully understand the task? Was your research thorough enough? Does your finished product meet the needs you identified and satisfy the criteria of your specification? Can you suggest any further improvements that could be made to your design? (See pages 56–57.)

Fig. 6.2 Pupils carrying out an evaluation

Ongoing Evaluation

Fig. 6.3

It is easy to think that evaluating only takes place at the end of a project. In fact this is not so. There is ongoing evaluation throughout the design process. It is very important that you evaluate at every stage of your project from identifying the need to making the finished product.

IDENTIFYING NEEDS AND OPPORTUNITES

When you are identifying needs and opportunities you will naturally evaluate them. You will probably choose to design a product that you like or you think will make a good activity for Design & Technology. Follow your instincts whenever you can as they will often lead you in the right direction.

GENERATING A DESIGN

When you are generating design proposals, you may need to fight against your natural instinct to reject unsuitable ideas. At this stage you must first make a list of as many ideas as possible. Once you have a range of ideas you can then evaluate them and decide which is the most suitable. (This is covered in detail on page 31.) When you have developed your design proposal from one of these ideas you should then evaluate this also.

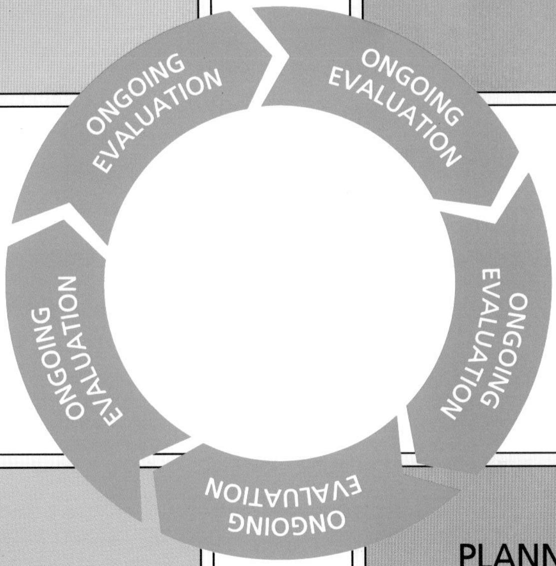

EVALUATING

Final Evaluation
Evaluation of the whole of your project (including evaluation of your finished product)

Evaluation as a starting point
Evaluation of existing artefacts, systems and environments.

PLANNING AND MAKING

During the planning and making stage, you will probably be evaluating your own skills and ability levels. You may choose to make a product because you know that you will be able to make it successfully. However, you may decide that you need to develop your abilities further by using skills you need to practise. Your teachers will encourage you to learn new techniques whenever possible so that you increase your range of skills.

Helpful Hints for Ongoing Evaluation

It is important to evaluate your work as it progresses. You should make notes and sketches throughout your project. This information can be used when you write your final evaluation. To help you with your ongoing evaluation, Fig. 6.4 shows a breakdown of the stages in a Design & Technology project and gives you a number of questions to ask yourself at each stage.

In D&T, you will learn to:
consider how well your products are designed and made
propose simple modifications to improve the effectiveness of designs and to overcome difficulties when making
reflect, individually and in groups, on how you went about your work and whether changes might be needed

Needs and opportunities
- Are the needs and opportunities that you have identified suitable for a Design & Technology project in school?
- Is your project too simple, or too ambitious?
- Do you have the knowledge, skills and materials required to complete the project?

Design brief
- Have you fully understood the task and what you have to do?
- It can be helpful to underline the key words in the design brief to make sure that you cover all parts of the brief fully.

Investigation
- How well have you investigated your project?
- Have you picked out the most important points to investigate?
- Have you done enough research, and was it thorough?
- You could begin your research by writing down what you already know about your topic and then identifying what you need to find out.
- Can you improve upon your research by using a variety of different research methods?

Specification
- Have you made a detailed list of the criteria that your product will have to satisfy?
- Have you listed them in order of importance?
- Have you broken down the criteria into those that are essential and those that are desirable?
- Remember to refer back to your specification as you work on your project.

Fig. 6.4

Ideas
- Have you produced a wide range of ideas?
- How have you decided which idea to develop into a design proposal?
- If you produced only one idea, have you explored and developed it fully?

Design proposal
- Have you checked that the design proposal satisfies the criteria of the specification?

Planning
- Have you planned your work in detail or have you begun to make it without any real planning?
- Are you able to follow your plan or does it need changing?
- Do not worry if you have to change your plan as you begin the making stage of your project. Make a note of the changes and, if necessary, replan what you have to do.

Making
- How successful have your preparations been?
- Is your time plan helpful and easy to follow?
- Don't forget to record what happens during the making process. Has the making of your final product gone according to plan?
- Are there any problems or snags? Have you made good use of all the technological equipment available to you?
- Have you included any information technology in your work?
- Have you made any changes to your finished product in the light of any investigations, experiments or accidents?
- Compare your finished product with your specification. Does it satisfy all of the criteria?

Don't be vague

Try not to give vague answers such as 'yes' or 'it did not taste very nice'.

Give reasons

Whenever possible, give a reason for your answer. For example, 'the vegetables were hard *because* I did not cook them for long enough'. If you give full and detailed answers they will form a good basis for your final evaluation.

Admit your mistakes

The evaluation is an important part of the design process and gives you the chance to find out more about yourself. As you write your notes don't be over critical – after all, no one's perfect. Try to be honest and admit your mistakes. You cannot lose marks for including them in your evaluation. You can gain marks if you show that you have learned how to avoid making the same mistake in the future.

Final Evaluation

The questions on pages 54–55 are intended to help you evaluate your work throughout the design process. This page should help you to evaluate your finished product. This will become part of your final evaluation which you put together at the end of the project.

Evaluating your finished product

To evaluate your finished product you need to have something to judge it against. If you have no comparison for your product your evaluation will consist of general statements that are vague and meaningless. Think back to the specification. Do you remember how you thought carefully about the criteria that the finished product must satisfy? You can now evaluate your finished product against those original criteria. Does it fulfil all the criteria in the specification or just some of them?

Fig. 6.5

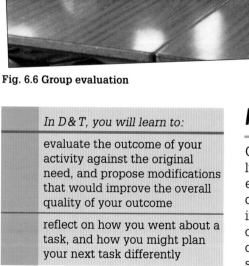

Fig. 6.6 Group evaluation

Other people's evaluation

You must always try to be objective when evaluating your own work. Sometimes it is easier to evaluate other people's work. Why not ask someone else to evaluate your finished product for you? Record their views and use the information in your final evaluation. You might decide to carry out a survey and see what several different people think about your design work.

In D&T, you will learn to:
evaluate the outcome of your activity against the original need, and propose modifications that would improve the overall quality of your outcome
reflect on how you went about a task, and how you might plan your next task differently

Improving your finished product

Could you improve your finished product in any way? You are either very lucky, or a very talented designer, if the answer to that question is no. Nearly every piece of work can be improved. It may be something simple such as changing the colour of the product, or it may be much more complicated and involve improving the product's performance. You may be given the opportunity not only to suggest improvements, but to carry them out. This will depend on how much time is available for the project. It is a good idea to leave some time at the end of a project to make improvements to your product.

An evaluation checklist

If you have recorded your work as it progressed you should not have any problems with evaluating the finished product. Fig. 6.7 shows a checklist which can be used to help you with your evaluation.

William Farr School	D&T

Evaluation

Compare your finished work with your specification.
Does it do what you wanted? **yes**

Write down the things you liked about it.
the variety and the taste

Write down the things you disliked about it.
the pitta bread was too much just to have on its own with the tuna

If you were going to do it again, what would you change?
How would you improve it?
I would make the filling of the pitta bread more exciting by putting ham and cucumber in one bit and tuna in the other

William Farr School – Design and Technology
Name **Alison Davidson** Form **7J**

Fig. 6.8 A directed-activity evaluation

William Farr School	D&T

Evaluation

I have compared my finished product with my specification and it seems to fulfil all the design criteria.
I worked individually when I was making my pyjama case but I did have a few problems actually producing it.
To test my final design, I put some clothes in it to see if it worked. I think my project has worked all right but I would probably change a few things if I made it again in order to make it easier to produce.
The hard thing about making my pyjama case was sewing round the corners.
The material I used was cotton satin.
I have learnt how to sew on press studs.
I think I have used my time wisely.

William Farr School – Design and Technology
Name **Joanne Wilson** Form **9W** Title **Storage** Sheet **5**

Fig. 6.9 An open-activity evaluation

Fig. 6.7

Checklist

1. What were my original aims?
2. How does my finished product meet these aims?
3. How successful is the product? Does it work?
4. Am I happy with the results?
5. What do other people think about my design work?
6. Can I improve the product in any way?

Presenting your final evaluation

The way in which you are required to present your final evaluation will depend upon your level of experience. Your early work in Design & Technology will probably be controlled or directed activities. This means that your teachers will be setting tasks for you to complete and showing you how to design things. Your first evaluation is likely to be written on your design worksheet. You may be given questions to answer about your finished product, the project and how you completed it (see Fig. 6.8).

As you progress and become more experienced, the evaluation will become a much larger part of your work. You will be expected to make notes and keep records as your work progresses and then use these to put together your final evaluation (see Fig. 6.9). Although your evaluation will be mainly a written piece of work, you should use sketches and diagrams to help to illustrate it. Remember to include what other people said about your work and don't forget to include any changes or improvements that could be made.

Testing

As part of your evaluation you may need to test your design. Testing can cover a variety of activities. Materials can be tested to see if they are suitable to use for a particular task. Finished products can be tested to see if they work successfully.

Testing and choosing materials

By testing materials you can find out more about their properties. For example, you may want to compare different materials to find out which is stronger, lighter or more hardwearing. These tests are known as **comparative tests** and the results will help you to decide which is the most suitable material to use for a particular design. Find out if there is any equipment in your school which can be used to test materials. It is possible to design and make simple test equipment yourself. Simple tests can be designed to see how fabrics resist stretching or abrasion.

Fig. 6.10 Pupils testing the strength of a piece of paper

Fig. 6.11

	In D & T, you will learn to:
	test simple objects to determine performance
	test simple objects you have made
	use different ways of assessing the effectiveness of a solution
	recognise that products must be electrically and mechanically safe

User testing

It is a good idea to let the people who are going to use your product test it for you. For example, if you have designed and made a toy or a game, why not let children test it and give you their reactions (see Fig. 6.11)? (N.B. First, make sure your product is safe.)

User testing is often carried out in industry before a new product is launched. Groups of potential users are asked for their reactions and opinions about a new product. Fig. 6.12 shows pupils involved in user testing as part of a project with a local supermarket.

Fig. 6.12

Fig. 6.13

Taste testing

To test a recipe or a food product that you have made you will need to taste it. People's tastes vary considerably and so it is worth asking a group of people to taste your food. This is called **taste testing**. Ask them to taste a small sample and write down their comments. They should include information about the colour, texture, smell and appearance of your food as well as the taste. You can record their comments on a simple chart and use the results to improve or change your work.

Product testing

Perhaps the best way to evaluate the success of your final product is to use it for what it is intended. Don't forget to keep a record of what happens during testing. It might be necessary for you to change or improve your product after it has been thoroughly tested. In industry, once the design work is complete, a limited number of products are produced for testing and evaluating. These are called **prototypes** and are designed to be tested so that any faults or problems can be found before large numbers of the product are manufactured. Prototypes are often tested to see if they are hardwearing. For example, washing machine prototypes are tested to see if they will continue working properly for many years. Designers learn a great deal from the results of the tests and use the information to improve their products.

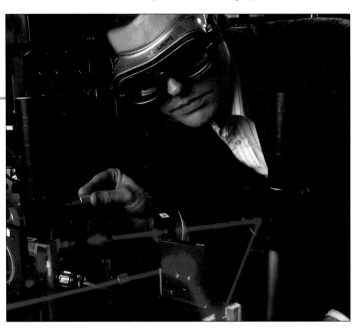
Fig. 6.14 Polymer testing at an IBM factory

Safety testing

As a designer you have a responsibility to the people who will use your products and to the environment. It is very important that what you design and make is safe to use and will not harm anyone. There are very strict rules and regulations which manufacturers in this country must keep. These are known as **British Standards**, and many products are stamped with the British Standard number which applies to them. For example, a 13-amp plug must be made so that it conforms to British Standard 1363A. Make sure that your products are as safe as possible, especially if they are to be used by young children.

Fig. 6.15 Testing the safety of a child's car seat

EXTRAS

What type of tests would you carry out on the following products?

1. A storage system for records, tapes and CDs.

2. A new recipe.

3. A working environment for an office.

Evaluating as a Starting Point

Design activities do not always have to begin with identifying needs and opportunities. Evaluating an existing artefact, system or environment can provide you with many opportunities for designing. You may choose to improve an existing product or you may decide to redesign it completely. Fig. 6.16 shows how evaluating can be the starting point for design work. (See page 14 also.)

Fig. 6.16

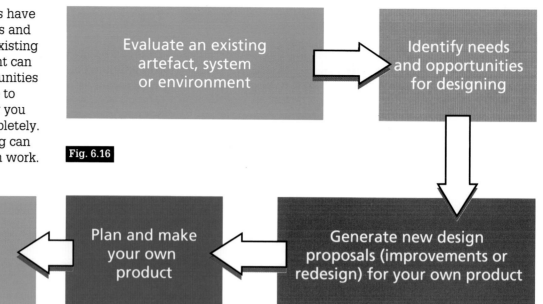

Evaluate an existing artefact, system or environment

→

Identify needs and opportunities for designing

↓

Generate new design proposals (improvements or redesign) for your own product

←

Plan and make your own product

←

Evaluate your own product

Evaluating in industry

As you have seen, evaluating other people's designs can be a starting point for a design activity. Designers in industry are often involved in redesigning existing products rather than creating new ones. Successful products are constantly evaluated, and updated when necessary. The changes made to the design may be due to one or more of the following:

- Falling sales.
- Changing styles and fashions.
- Incorporating new technology into the product and the method of producing it.
- Selling the product from a different angle. For example, a manufacturer may decide to stress that an existing product is environmentally friendly to attract customers who are concerned about the environment.
- Competition from rival products forcing changes to be made. Manufacturers need to keep ahead of their competitors in product design if they are to keep their share of the market.

In D & T, you will learn to:
analyse a system to determine its effectiveness and suggest improvements
investigate existing solutions to design and technological problems when developing ideas for new ones
propose modifications to improve the performance and appeal of existing products
make judgements about products designed and made by others

Fig. 6.17 The changing design of telephone boxes

Checklist Fig. 6.18

1. What were the designer's original aims? Draw up what you think was their design specification.

2. How well does the product meet the specification?

3. How well does the product work?

4. How well is the product made?

5. What materials have been used for the product? Are they suitable?

6. Is the product environmentally friendly?

7. What improvements to the product can you suggest?

Once you have a good understanding of the product and its function, you can begin to suggest improvements that may be made. Sometimes a minor alteration can make a product more efficient. Don't forget that a product can be a system or an environment as well as an artefact. You can evaluate them all in a very similar way.

Evaluating an existing product

Evaluating an existing product will enable you to learn a lot about designing. You can study how other designers have made use of the materials and the technology available to them when making their product.

You should begin to evaluate a product by studying it carefully and then trying to work out the designer's original aims. If possible, draw up your own specification for the product. You can then check if the product meets the original aims. It may be possible for you to test the product to find out how it was made and how well it works (see Fig. 6.18).

Fig. 6.19

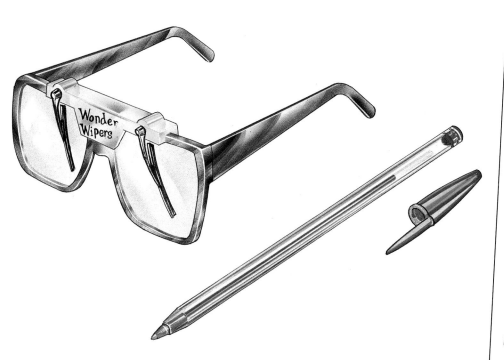

Fig. 6.20

Product analysis exercise

Fig. 6.20 shows two very different products – a pair of 'Wonder Wipers' glasses and a ballpoint pen. Look at them and think about each of them very carefully. Use the checklist in Fig. 6.18 to evaluate them. Then answer the following additional questions. Which of the two products do you think will sell more (a) in the short-term? and (b) in the long-term? Why?

What technological problems do you think the designer of the 'Wonder Wipers' might have had?

Can you think of any ways in which the ballpoint pen might be improved?

7 D & T AND THE ENVIRONMENT

Since earliest times people have had an important relationship with their environment. It has provided them with food, water and shelter. There are parts of the world, such as deserts and the polar regions, where the environment makes it difficult, if not impossible, for people to live. These areas have remained virtually unchanged for millions of years.

Changing the environment

Design involves people in changing their environment. You change your environment every time you tidy your room or your desk. Everyone is a designer at one time or another. People have been changing their environment in order to meet their needs ever since they have lived on the earth. They made paths and tracks as they hunted for food, cut down trees and reeds to make shelters, and cleared forests to plant crops.

Fig. 7.1 An environment unchanged for millions of years

The landscape

Over the centuries the British landscape has changed. Large areas of Britain were once covered with forests which have since disappeared. As technology gradually developed more changes took place. People discovered how to use materials, like stone and metal, to make tools. Soon they were able to make quite sophisticated buildings in which to live instead of caves and huts. Villages and settlements gradually developed and the environment was changed for ever. Many of the fields and hedges that are seen today are the result of people enclosing their farm lands as a response to the Enclosure Acts of the eighteenth century.

Fig. 7.2 Field patterns set out in the eighteenth century

With the rise in population and the Industrial Revolution many towns increased in size and became overcrowded. After the Second World War new towns were planned and built within a short time. They were needed to ease the overcrowding in the towns and cities and to provide houses for thousands of families who had lost their homes during the war. Later, a whole new city, Milton Keynes, was planned and built in Buckinghamshire.

In D & T, you will learn to:

investigate the effects of design and technological activity on the environment and take account of its impact

Fig. 7.3a Buckinghamshire countryside before Milton Keynes was built

Fig. 7.3b Milton Keynes

Towns and cities

Towns and cities are environments in themselves. Once they were dirty and unpleasant places, but conditions have improved as technology has been used to clean up industrial areas and divert traffic from city centres. Many town centres have pedestrianised shopping areas which are free from traffic. On the outskirts of towns and cities shopping malls have been built. These malls are easily accessible by road and train, have ample parking space and, once inside the mall, shoppers are protected from the weather. In recent years designers and planners have made a considerable effort to improve the environment of towns. Disused industrial areas and derelict sites have been given a new lease of life by the building of offices, shops and houses. High-rise flats are being knocked down and replaced with more suitable housing.

Fig. 7.4 The interior of the Metro shopping mall in Gateshead

Housing

Many people's home environments have been improved considerably in recent years. It is not so long ago that many homes had outside toilets and no bathrooms. Often the only form of heating was an open fire in the main rooms. Consider how this compares with houses of today with their central heating, double glazing and energy-saving insulation.

Fig. 7.5

Transport

It used to be very uncomfortable and dangerous to travel around the country. With the invention of the petrol engine and the design of the motor car, an improved road system was needed. Nowadays, it is possible to travel from one part of the country to another safely, quickly and conveniently. Isolated places can be reached easily, and journeys which once took several days can be made in just a few hours. Modern roads and motorways have their advantages but they have also changed the environment.

Fig. 7.6

EXTRAS

1. Talk to some elderly friends or relations and find out what their home environment was like when they were your age. How did they heat their home? Where were the toilets? What labour-saving devices did they have to help them with their domestic chores? Compare their lifestyle with yours.

Historical and Cultural Background

People have always used technology to make their lives easier. The earliest forms of technology used were all labour-saving devices – for example, the wedge, the lever and the inclined plane (see Fig. 7.7 a, b and c). Archaeologists have discovered that they were used by Stone Age people over 100,000 years ago.

Fig. 7.7c The inclined plane

Fig. 7.8 A shadoof

Fig. 7.7a The wedge

Fig. 7.7b The lever

One of the earliest stone tools was the wedge. It was first used as a simple hand axe for digging, splitting and shaping wood, and cutting up food. It was later fitted to a wooden handle so that it was much more powerful. The lever and the inclined plane were used to move large blocks of stone. They were probably used to build Stonehenge and large buildings, such as the Pyramids.

These examples of early technology are still used today and form the basis on which many of our modern machines work. In some countries they are used in the same way as they were thousands of years ago. For example, the shadoof (see Fig. 7.8) was designed to help draw water from deep wells. It consists of a lever with a bucket on one end and a counter weight on the other. It is still used today to irrigate the dry land in parts of Egypt.

The Industrial Revolution

During the eighteenth and early nineteenth centuries, a considerable amount of change took place in technology, the environment and people's lives. This period in history is called the **Industrial Revolution**. It began when a number of machines were designed which improved the production of textiles. Eventually machines were made which could weave large amounts of cloth very quickly. At first these machines were driven by water power but it soon became possible to use steam engines to power them. Large factories or mills were built to house the machines and many people moved from the country to the towns to work in the factories.

Also during the eighteenth century a method was found of using coal or coke (produced from coal) as a fuel for the iron-making process.

This, combined with the coal needed by the steam engines, increased the demand for coal considerably. New mines were built to help satisfy the demand and new mining towns and villages grew up in the areas where coal was plentiful. The coal had to be moved from the mines to the towns and factories so canals and, later, railways were built to transport it.

The towns expanded rapidly and soon became dirty and overcrowded. People often lived in very unhealthy conditions with poor sanitation and little privacy. Conditions in the mills, factories and coal mines were no better. The hours were long and the work was hard and often dangerous.

By using technology, Britain became the first industrial nation. However, it did so at an enormous cost to both its people and its environment. A great deal can be learnt from the Industrial Revolution about the moral and social responsibility of using technology.

Fig. 7.9 Manchester in the 1850s

> *In D & T, you will learn to:*
>
> recognise the historical and cultural background to design and technological developments

The electronic age

At the present time, another technological revolution is taking place. This would probably not have happened without a material known as silicon. It is used to make a variety of electronic components including transistors and microchips. Microchips (also known as integrated circuits) are used in a lot of the appliances that we use every day and take for granted, such as computers, watches and washing machines.

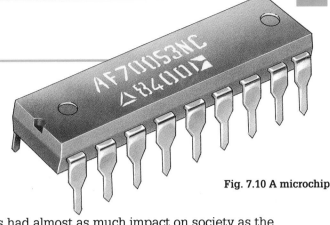

Fig. 7.10 A microchip

The microchip has had almost as much impact on society as the Industrial Revolution did. Technology has taken another giant leap forward but the effects have been far less damaging. People have gained from the technological development in many ways, such as better medical care and more efficient communication. The environment has suffered less because there are now planning regulations and people are more aware of the problems of pollution than they were in the past.

Above Fig. 7.11a A silicon chip

Right Fig. 7.11b A slice of silicon showing the chips before cutting

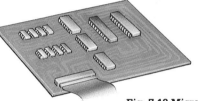

Fig. 7.12 Microchips in a printed circuit board (PCB)

Appropriate technology

It is very important that the technology used is appropriate for the people who are using it. The technology of many developing countries is not as advanced as in the West. In India, old British motor cars and motor cycles are still made and used. This is because they suit the needs of the people and the level of technology available in most parts of the country. These vehicles are relatively easy and cheap to produce and simple to maintain. If western countries give modern vehicles to developing countries as part of an aid package, it is essential that they also provide the maintenance skills and spare parts to ensure that the vehicles have a long life.

Fig. 7.13 Transport in India

EXTRAS

1. Think about your own lifestyle. Make a list of any modern tools you use that are based on the wedge, the lever and the inclined plane.

2. Make a list of the technological appliances you use regularly which contain microchips.

Moral Responsibility for Technology

Technology affects people and the environment. It must, therefore, be used in a responsible way if everyone is to benefit from it.

Technology should be used to make the world a better place to live in but, unfortunately, this is not always the case. In India in 1986, many people died or were seriously injured following an accident at the Bhopal chemical works. In the same year thousands of people throughout Europe were affected by radiation following an accident at a nuclear power station at Chernobyl in Ukraine. During the 1991 Gulf War, large amounts of oil were spilled into the Persian Gulf. This area will take many years to recover from this ecological disaster. Every year, 300 million gallons of raw, or partially treated, sewage is pumped into British seas. This not only damages the sea environment but also poses a threat to human health.

Fig. 7.14 An ecological disaster

Fig. 7.15 A dangerous toy

Product safety

Designers have a responsibility for their products. They must be safe and not harm the user. Most products made nowadays have to go through tests before they are allowed to be sold. Sometimes products which do not conform to the proper safety standards get on to the market, especially at Christmas time. You have probably seen warnings on television about some types of imported soft toys which may be harmful. Great care needs to be taken when designing products, especially those for babies and small children. Toys with small parts which can easily be broken off and swallowed can be extremely dangerous.

Product research

A lot has been done in recent years to make the products we use much safer. For example, a considerable amount of research has taken place in order to improve the safety of motor cars. Modern cars now have 'crumple zones' which are designed to absorb the impact of a collision and protect the driver and passengers. If you compare the interior design of a modern car with that of a car built thirty years ago you will notice that the modern one is much safer. The old-fashioned metal dashboards have been replaced with softer, plastic ones and many of the controls have been designed so that they do not cause injury in an accident.

Fig. 7.16 Aerial view of a car being crash-tested

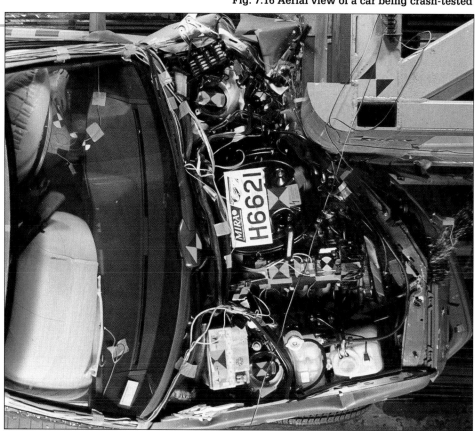

In D&T, you will learn to:

recognise that economic, moral, social and environmental factors can influence design and technological activities

Social Responsibility for Technology

Designers have a responsibility to society and this affects what they produce. They must make sure that the changes they bring about by using technology benefit everyone and improve their environment or lifestyle.

Fig. 7.17

Domestic technology

Many of the technological developments which make life easier have already been taken for granted - for example, the washing machine, the microwave cooker and the dishwasher. Washing your clothes can now be done in a couple of hours. It can even be done while you are asleep, using low cost electricity. This not only makes life easier but makes the task more energy-efficient too. When you arrive home from school you no longer need to wait a long time for something to eat. A pre-prepared meal can be put into the microwave and, within a few minutes, you can be eating your favourite meal.

Medical technology

Technology has been used to improve the medical care that we receive. Generally, people are living much longer than they were a hundred years ago. Hospitals make considerable use of technology in their day-to-day running. Intensive care wards use electronic equipment to monitor the condition of their patients, while technological equipment is used to find out what illness a patient has. Lasers are being used more and more to carry out operations. This helps to prevent the risk of infection and allows the patient to recover more quickly. Technology allows preventative medicine to be carried out. Many health centres have clinics where people's blood pressure and cholesterol levels can be checked and monitored. This helps to prevent illnesses such as heart disease.

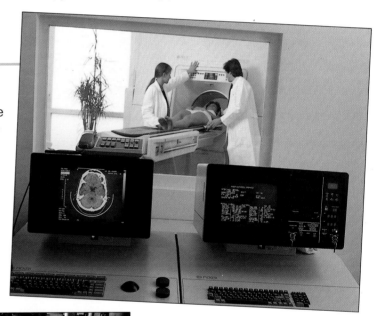
Fig. 7.18 A brain scanner

Information technology

The use of technology at work has brought about many changes. In work places word processors have replaced the typewriter. Word processors allow you to see what you have written before you print it on to paper. Portable telephones, fax machines and laptop computers have also changed the way people work. Some people no longer need to go to the office or factory but are able to work from home, in their car or on the train. This type of technology is known as information technology and is sometimes referred to as IT. You can find out more about IT from another book in this series called *What's IT all about?*

Fig. 7.19

Leisure technology

The way people use their leisure time shows the many ways in which technology has changed their lifestyle. Television, video recorders, computer games and compact discs all help to make life more enjoyable.

EXTRAS

1. Discuss in a group why you think it is important for designers to use technology to improve the quality of peoples' lives.

Looking after the Environment

Fig. 7.20

As a designer you will want to improve your surroundings and take great care not to damage the environment. There is a natural balance between people, animals, plants and the environment which is known as the **ecosystem**. Using the world's resources carefully and keeping the air and water free from pollution are both ways in which we can help to keep this balance. The twentieth century has been a time of rapid technological growth and it is now becoming clear that this growth can easily affect the ecosystem. Many people are now becoming aware of the need to protect the Earth from the damaging effects caused by misusing its resources.

Resources

The fuels used to heat homes and run cars are examples of resources. Materials such as wood and metals, are also resources. Some resources can be replaced, but others cannot – these are called non-renewable resources. Metals and fuels which are taken out of the ground, such as coal and gas, are examples of non-renewable resources. To help you think about resources try the following task.

Think about the fuels used to heat your home. Using a computer, or graph paper, make a chart to show the different types of fuels used by your class members to heat their home. Work out what percentage use gas, electricity, solid fuel or other resources, such as solar power.

Your results will almost certainly show that the Earth's fossil fuels, such as coal, oil and gas are the most popular ways of heating your homes. There are two main reasons why the use of fossil fuels should be limited.

First, they are being used up at an alarming rate. Can you suggest any reasons for this? Second, when fossil fuels are burnt they give off the gas carbon dioxide which can harm the environment and eventually upset the ecosystem.

Fig. 7.21

The greenhouse effect

The carbon dioxide from burnt fossil fuels adds to the **greenhouse effect** which keeps the Earth's atmosphere warm (see Fig. 7.22). If the effect becomes too strong, it could cause world temperatures to rise and climate patterns to change. Any changes in the climate could cause serious flooding in some parts of the world and severe drought in other parts. Chlorofluorocarbons (CFCs), which are used in some aerosol sprays and refrigerators also add to the greenhouse effect. Some products which are sold in aerosol cans state on them that they are 'CFC-free' or 'environmentally friendly'.

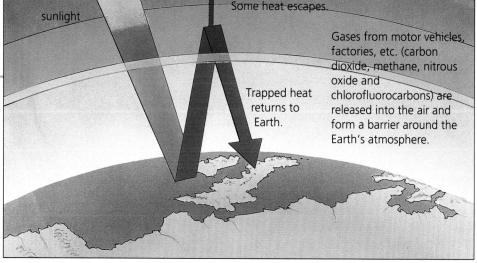

sunlight

Some heat escapes.

Gases from motor vehicles, factories, etc. (carbon dioxide, methane, nitrous oxide and chlorofluorocarbons) are released into the air and form a barrier around the Earth's atmosphere.

Trapped heat returns to Earth.

Fig. 7.22 The greenhouse effect

In D & T, you will learn to:
recognise that economic, moral, social and environmental factors can influence design and technological activities

Everyone can help to reduce the greenhouse effect by using CFC-free products and by disposing of old refrigerators safely. Some electrical shops will now take away old appliances and recycle the refrigerant.

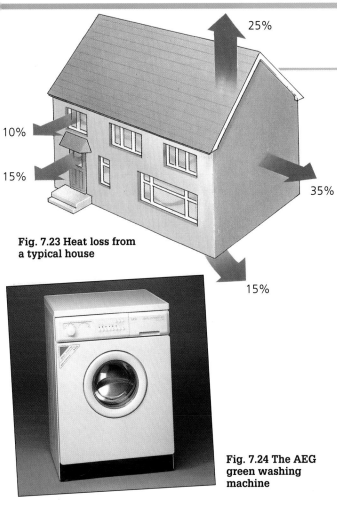

25%

10%

15%

35%

15%

Fig. 7.23 Heat loss from a typical house

Fig. 7.24 The AEG green washing machine

Saving resources

In the United Kingdom about £7 billion of energy is wasted every year. You can help to save resources by saving energy. There are many ways in which you and your family can make your house an energy-saving home. Here are a few. Can you think of any others?

● Take a shower instead of a bath.

● Turn off the lights when you leave a room.

● Use a washing machine that has a half load button and one that will wash at a lower temperature.

● Insulate your home by lagging pipes, fitting draught excluders around doors and windows and putting insulating material in the loft.

● Set the thermostats on radiators and heating systems to a slightly lower room temperature.

You could choose environmentally friendly household products and use only those which are free from CFCs. It is now possible to buy domestic machines that use less energy to operate. The AEG 'green' washing machine is computer-controlled to regulate the amount of water and electricity used. A full load is washed at 60 °C rather than 95 °C which saves a third of the electricity. The energy costs of gas-powered tumble dryers are only a third of those of a similar machine run on electricity.

Recycling

Another good way to save the Earth's resources is to recycle some of the waste. You may already be aware of the efforts of some charity organisations who raise money by collecting and selling aluminium cans, newspaper and glass for recycling. Recycling materials uses less energy than making new materials. Fig. 7.25 shows how recycling aluminium drinks cans can save up to 95% of the energy costs.

Millions of tonnes of household waste are produced each year and much of it comes from packaging. Each person in Great Britain throws away about a third of a tonne of waste every year. Waste that will rot away in time is known as **biodegradable** but most waste either has to be buried or burnt. However, many items are made from a mixture of both biodegradable and non-biodegradable materials. If these materials are to be recycled

they need to be separated from each other. This can be a difficult and time-consuming operation. In the future, perhaps households will have a series of dustbins, one for each type of material.

Finding other uses for things is another form of recycling. An example of this is using an empty tin to store your pencils. This is a very effective form of recycling because there are no costs involved, either in terms of energy or damage to the environment. Look out for items which can be re-used in other ways. Your teachers will probably have examples of this to show you in the classroom – old washing-up

liquid bottles are sometimes used as glue pots and old aerosol lids make excellent containers for paper clips or drawing pins.

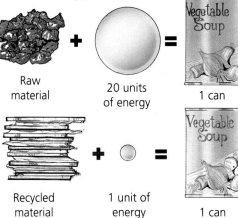

Raw material + 20 units of energy = 1 can

Recycled material + 1 unit of energy = 1 can

Fig. 7.25 Recycled cans save energy

EXTRAS

1. Carry out a survey of things you throw away at home. How much of it could be recycled or reused? Show your results in a chart or graph.

Conflict

Technology must be used carefully in order to keep the changes it causes at a level which is acceptable to most people. Sometimes the use of technology can bring people into conflict with each other. Problems can occur when the needs of individual people conflict with those of society. For example, individual people might want the freedom of their own transport but society in general does not want more roads, a polluted atmosphere and town centres choked with traffic. Many people want to own their own homes away from town centres and industrial areas but people living in small villages often object to the building of housing estates near them.

Conflict can also be caused when the solution to one problem causes another problem. Designers must take great care to make sure that the

Fig. 7.26 Trees being damaged by acid rain

products they design do not cause other people new problems. People who live in the Scandinavian countries have suffered for many years from the effects of smoke from the factories and power stations in Great Britain. The fumes are blown across the North Sea where the sulphur dioxide they contain dissolves in the moisture in the atmosphere and eventually falls as acid rain. Forests can be damaged by only a small amount of acid rain which then runs into the lakes and kills fish and other animals.

Solving problems for the people of one country is causing problems for people of another.

Health care

The advances in medical technology that have taken place in the last century have had an important effect on most people. People are on average living much longer than they were last century. Fewer babies die at birth and cures have been found for diseases which were once fatal. More people are living longer after retiring from work than ever before. As more people retire, the working population gets smaller and the non-working population increases. Therefore, there are a greater number of people who need to be cared for and supported by the rest of society.

The diagram in Fig. 7.27a shows the population of a developing country. Compare it with the population of a developed country in Fig. 7.27b and you will see that more people are living longer in the developed country. This is due to the advances in medical technology.

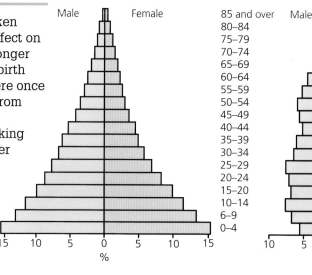

Fig. 7.27a Population of a developing country

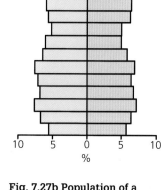

Fig. 7.27b Population of a developed country

Transport

In order to improve transportation around Great Britain one solution is to build longer and wider roads. However, this means destroying

	In D & T, you will learn to:
	recognise potential conflicts between the needs of individuals and of society
	recognise that a solution may result in problems in other areas

large areas of hedgerows and other natural habitats, and at the same time encouraging the use of fossil fuels. For example, the proposed East Coast Expressway would improve the road network between Scotland and the South East of England and access to the Channel Tunnel but only at considerable cost to the environment. Discouraging the use of the roads by increasing tax and fuel costs may be good for the environment but they are not

popular with some people who believe it limits their freedom to travel. Many city councils are considering reducing the number of vehicles using city centre roads by making drivers pay to use them. Some areas are introducing 'park and ride' schemes in which commuters drive to car parks on the outskirts of towns and cities. They then continue their journey into the centre of the town or city in special buses.

Fig. 7.28 A combine harvester operated by a small workforce

Agriculture

In the last fifty years farming has become a highly technological industry. Modern agricultural machines can be operated by a small workforce and can harvest and plant crops very quickly. To make these machines more efficient hedgerows have been removed to make the fields larger. This has affected the environment and destroyed the natural habitat of many plants and animals. Chemicals are also used to help produce bigger crops and make the land more productive. This can cause problems if the chemicals find their way into the water supply. There are areas of the country where nitrate levels in the drinking water are very high. It is fortunate that there are some farmers who believe that organic methods of farming, with careful management, can be as productive and profitable as non-organic farming.

New technology

Conflict can also occur when new technology is introduced too quickly. People often feel that their livelihood is being threatened. In the past the introduction of new machines and techniques has even caused riots and revolts. In the early nineteenth century the Luddites destroyed the new textile machines. Some people may have felt threatened when computers and information technology began to be used where they worked. The introduction of new technology needs to be carefully managed so that it does not frighten people. Some jobs may disappear, but new ones are created – programmers and software engineers, for example. Technology should be applied in such a way that it benefits people rather than making them feel threatened.

Above: Fig. 7.29
The Luddites rioting

Power generation

The way in which electrical power is produced is a subject which can cause conflict between people. Should electricity continue to be generated by the burning of fossil fuels such as coal and oil? It is using up valuable resources, causing pollution and damaging the environment. One alternative is to use nuclear power to provide electricity. However, the accident at the nuclear power station at Chernobyl in the Ukraine highlighted some of the dangers of this method. People are worried about the effects of radiation and its possible link with illnesses like leukaemia. Disposing of the waste from nuclear power stations is also a problem. Plutonium, the radioactive waste from nuclear power generation, is thought to be dangerous for thousands of years and so must be disposed of very carefully.

Fig. 7.30 Fossil fuels or nuclear fuels?

EXTRAS

1. Find out more information about the production of electrical power from fossil fuels and by nuclear power generation. What are the advantages and disadvantages of each process?

Major Road Works

Traffic congestion causes problems in many busy towns and villages and local residents often campaign for relief roads to be constructed to by-pass the centre of the town or the village. Although this kind of solution may be of benefit to many people there could be disadvantages or costs to others.

Before any plans can be drawn up for the building of a new road, a lot of research has to be done to prove that a new road is the best solution to the problems caused by traffic congestion. Evidence has to be collected to show on which roads serious congestion occurs and the kind of vehicles that use it. Road accident statistics will have to be consulted to find out if there are any accident blackspots which could be improved by building a by-pass.

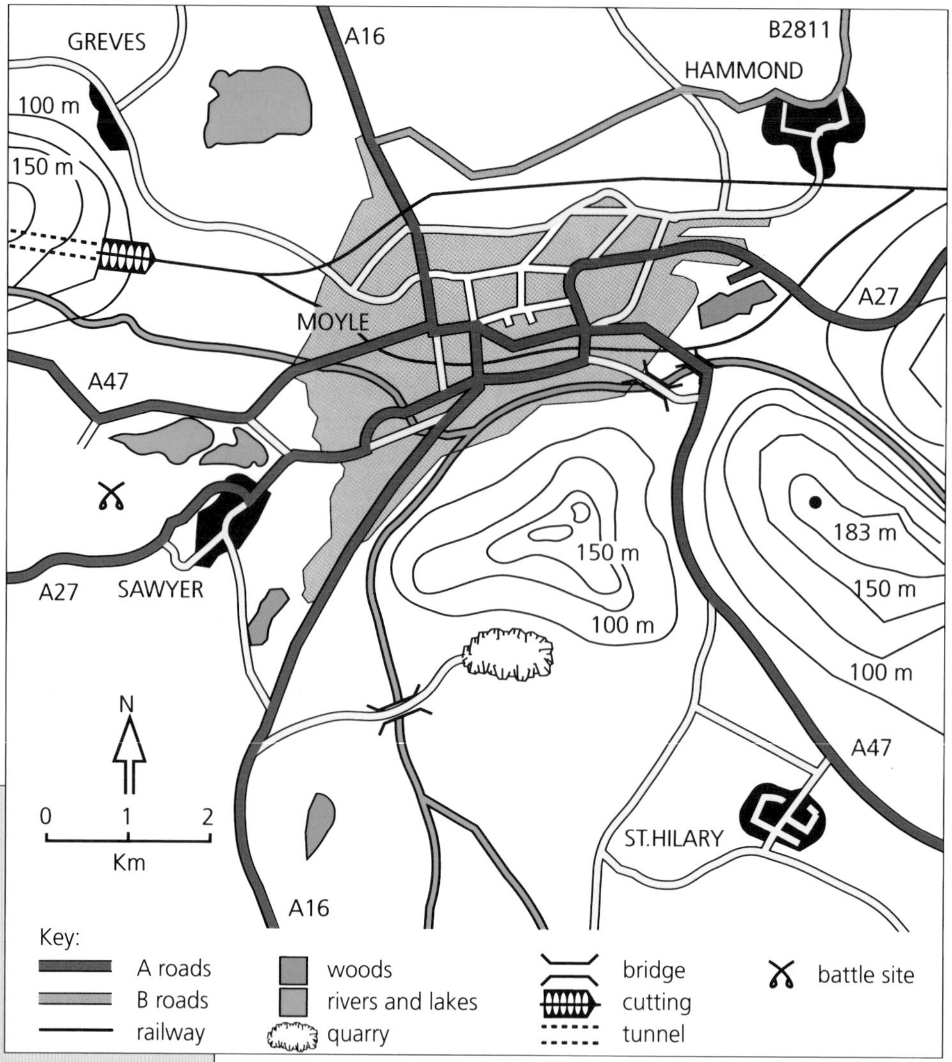

Fig. 7.31 The town of Moyle and the surrounding area

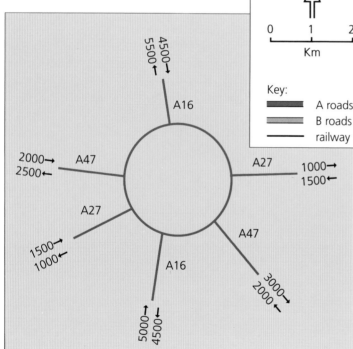

Fig. 7.32 Approximate daily traffic flow into and out of Moyle on the main roads

Land use

A careful study of land use is necessary to establish the ownership and current use of the land on which it is proposed to site the new road. If the land is privately owned will the owner be willing to sell? If not, a compulsory purchase order may be necessary and compensation will have to be paid.

Geological survey

The physical geography of the area must be taken into account when deciding possible routes for a road. Before a new road can be constructed engineers need to be aware of the geological features of the land over which the road is to be built – it could be granite, alluvium, sand and gravel, or clay, for example. This information can be obtained from geological maps and bore holes that have already been drilled. New bore holes can be drilled but it is an expensive process, so these should be kept to a minimum. This geological information will affect engineering decisions, such as the depth and strength of the foundations of the by-pass and the amount of drainage required.

Pollution

Consideration must be given to air and noise pollution from vehicles. There is evidence that exhaust fumes are harmful to people living near busy roads. Experts believe that exposure to the lead found in vehicle exhausts can cause brain damage in young children. Motor vehicles make more noise when accelerating. Therefore it can be very noisy living near to roundabouts and traffic lights because of traffic accelerating away from these areas.

Ecology

Careful research needs to be carried out into the ecology of the land that is to be built on. The land may be protected because it contains footpaths, a national park or an area of outstanding beauty. It may also include protected wildlife which could be damaged by building of a by-pass. The environmental organisation, Friends of the Earth, are concerned that many sites of special scientific interest (SSSI) have already been damaged by new roads and planned roads could damage many more. These sites are vital for the preservation of wildlife. They also provide areas for the scientific study of the environment.

1. It has already been decided that the town of Moyle needs a by-pass. In your groups study the information given on these pages. Then work out a suitable route for the by-pass.

2. Work out an approximate cost for your proposals using the figures given. Remember that there are other costs in addition to the financial ones to be taken into account. Make a list of these other costs.

Construction costs
Bridge	£0.125m each
Culvert	£0.05m each
Cutting	£0.10m per km
Embankment	£0.05m per km
Road base	£0.10m per km
Road top surface	£0.05m per km
Roundabout	£0.05m each
Underpass	£0.125m each

3. Make a presentation to your class of your chosen route showing why you chose it and the costs and benefits of constructing your by-pass. Include information about who you think will gain or profit from this by-pass and who might be harmed or damaged by it.

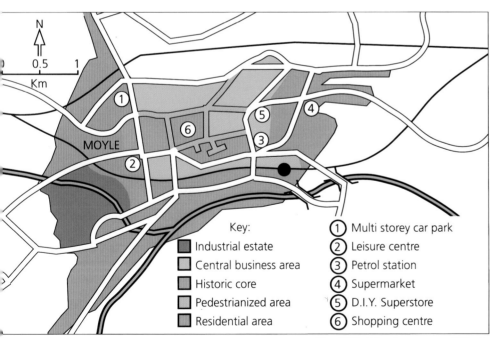

Key:
- Industrial estate
- Central business area
- Historic core
- Pedestrianized area
- Residential area

① Multi storey car park
② Leisure centre
③ Petrol station
④ Supermarket
⑤ D.I.Y. Superstore
⑥ Shopping centre

Fig. 7.33 A land use map of Moyle

Local businesses

Although many of the residents in a town may benefit from the building of a relief road some local businesses could suffer because of the re-routing of traffic away from the town. For example, a large proportion of the customers of some petrol stations are people who are just driving through the town on their way to somewhere else.

A Japanese Experience

A

The photographs on these pages show the products resulting from a Design & Technology activity on Japan. The Year 8 pupils involved in this activity discovered many differences between Japanese and European cultures. The activity began with a video about life in Japan. Japanese people from the local car factory were invited to come and talk about life in their home country. This was followed by a visit to the factory to see the influence that Japanese culture had on the oriental people's attitude to life. The projects that followed this introduction were both varied and new to most pupils.

One group of pupils created the traditional Japanese living room shown in photograph **A**. The pupils are wearing kimonos which were made by Year 12 pupils at the school. As you can see from the photograph, it is traditional to sit on the floor at a very low table.

Photograph **B** shows a display of the pupils' investigation into Japanese food and culture. The pupils discovered that, although you can buy McDonald's and Kentucky Fried Chicken takeaways in Japan, traditional Japanese food is very different from British food. Sushi, which is raw fish, and tempura, which consists of fried vegetables and seafood, are both very popular dishes.

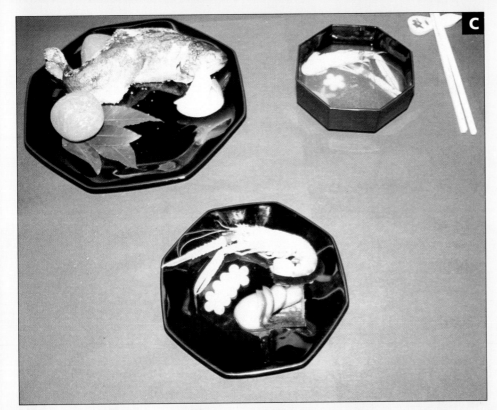

A local restaurateur was invited to the school to demonstrate the art of Japanese food preparation. The visit encouraged the pupils to experiment with Japanese dishes, both at school and at home. Photograph **C** shows that a great deal of care is taken with the presentation of the food. Notice how beautifully the vegetables are cut, so that they look like flowers.

Photograph **D** shows a range of products made during the activity on Japan. One group of pupils discovered that, compared with learning the 26 characters of the English alphabet, an 11-year-old Japanese pupil would have learned 800 characters of the Japanese alphabet. By the age of 16, a pupil would know 2000 Japanese characters. The pupils looked at picture scrolls, called emaki, and at haiku, a form of Japanese poetry. They produced Japanese writing using paintbrushes. They did not understand the writing as it was very complex, but they thought that it was very decorative. You can see examples of their Japanese writing in photograph D.

Photograph **E** shows two pairs of mules, which were designed and made by the pupils. It is considered impolite to enter any Japanese building in outdoor shoes, so mules are worn inside the building instead.

F Following a mini-course on origami (paper sculpture), some pupils designed and made traditional Japanese card lunch boxes, called icki-ben. Some of these are shown in photograph **F**. Other pupils made different origami products, such as colourful birds with moving wings.

Photograph **G** shows examples of the traditional art of silk painting. Pupils painted and dyed samples of silk. They then mounted these on card to produce interesting and unusual greetings cards.

G

Some British schools have developed strong links with Japanese schools, through the assistance of the Japan Information Office. Japanese children have sent photographs of everyday Japanese artefacts, such as bus tickets, chopsticks, tableware, fans, futons, kimonos, kites, lanterns, masks and bank notes. Following the activity on Japan, the pupils at this school are hoping to form links with a school in Japan. They are collecting items which they can use to inform Japanese pupils of the British way of life.

Toys and Games

The photographs on these pages show toys and games that have been made by Year 8 and Year 9 pupils.

Photograph **A** shows toys made by some Year 8 pupils. They began their activity by investigating toys for very young children. They carried out their research on the toys of younger members of their own families. The products that they have made range from toys that are active, like the push-along duck and the fire engine, to toys that are cuddly, like the spider and the ladybird. The pupils have used a range of materials and techniques to produce attractive brightly-coloured toys that will appeal to young children. It is always important to consider carefully who you are making the product for. Look again at the toys in photograph A. Do you think that they are all suitable for very young children?

The games in photograph **B** have been made by another group of Year 8 pupils. They decided to look at small games to entertain children. They have used mainly wood and acrylic for the games. When acrylic is cleaned and polished, it becomes bright and attractive. Wood can be finished in many ways – here it has been stained, painted and varnished. It is very important to consider safety when finishing toys and games that young children will be using. Young children often put things into their mouths and some finishes can be harmful.

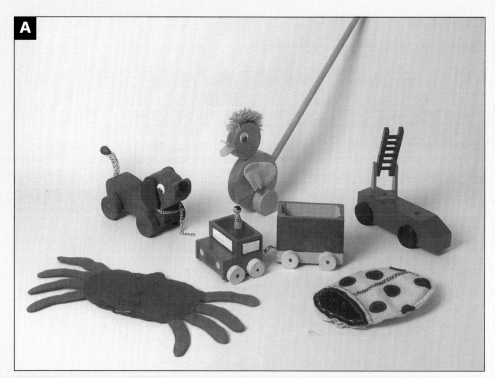

A

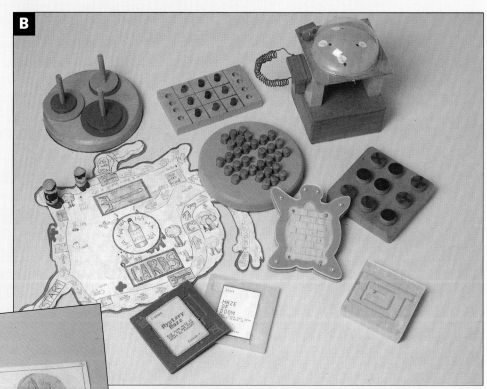

B

C

Photograph **C** shows some of the stages involved in making one of the above games.

D

E

F

Photographs **D**, **E** and **F** show mechanical toys made by Year 9 pupils. They have used materials, such as fabric, wood and metal, and different mechanisms to make the toys. The body of the puppet in photograph **D** is made of wooden linkages, held together with wire. The little man in photograph **E** climbs up and down his pole, using no more than a simple nut on a long bolt. The man's arms and legs are pin-jointed. In photograph **F**, the cheerful character on the trolley waves his arms up and down as he is pulled along. The arms are connected to a cranked front axle in order to achieve this movement.

Mechanisms can often be used to make toys interesting and fun. Before actually making these toys the pupils modelled them, using card and pieces of wood, to see if the toys would work as intended. It is always a good idea to model a mechanical device before making the finished product, as the design often needs to be modified.

India

India has been used as a theme for many Design & Technology activities at this school. Photographs **A** to **E** show an Indian Bazaar that one group of Year 7 pupils organised. As well as selling the products that they had made, the pupils put on entertainment, including dancing and snake charming. The activity involved all aspects of technology. It was also linked with the humanities department, as one of their 'foreign places' activities.

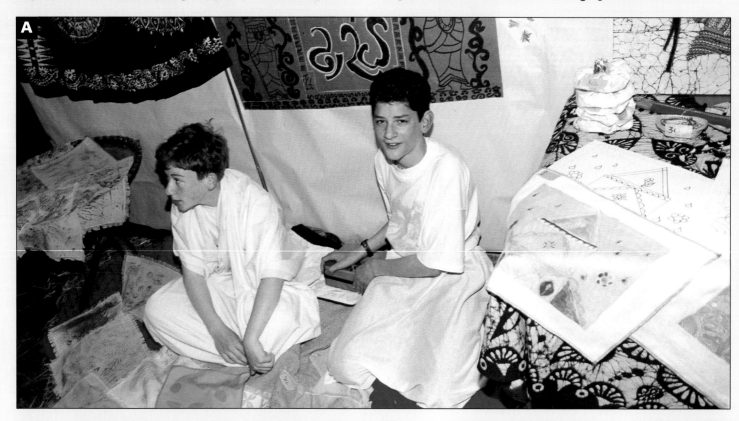

Photograph **A** shows pupils wearing national costume and seated in their Bazaar booth. They are selling textile samples that have been produced in Indian style.

Photographs **B** and **C** show an elephant costume, made from colourful textiles. This formed the centre-piece in the Bazaar entertainment.

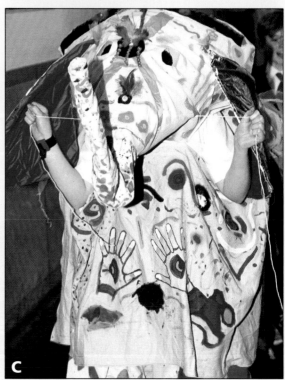

Photograph **D** shows more pupils wearing Indian costume. They are selling products that have been made by the pupils. The products have been made from both metal and wood. Look at the designs on them. Can you see the Indian influence in the decoration? Some of the pupils' design work can be seen on the wall behind the stall.

At one stall, pupils were demonstrating the art of silk painting. You can see this in photograph **E**.

Looking at the culture of a country would not be complete without a study of the country's food and cooking. The pupils investigated the different methods of Indian cooking, and contrasted these with the cooking methods of western cultures. Photograph **F** shows a display of some Indian dishes, together with spices and typical vegetables.

As the Indian Bazaar involved buying and selling goods, an extension to this activity would be to compare methods of trade and business in India with those in Britain.

Environments

Environments can provide the starting point for a wide range of Design & Technology activities. It is not always possible to make the actual environment that you design. The finished project may be too large or too expensive for you to produce in school, so you may have to make a presentation model instead.

Photograph **A** shows a model of a golf course that a Year 9 pupil has designed and made. The scale model could be used to allow prospective clients of the golf club to view the new development. Brochures were also produced to highlight the features of the course.

The context of the home provides a number of opportunities for designing. The model of a kitchen shown in photograph **B** has been produced by Year 9 pupils. The fittings can be moved around the room, allowing different layouts to be explored. A visit to a local museum may enable pupils to compare kitchen designs of the past with those of today. Kitchen equipment has also changed. A museum may display a range of mechanical inventions from the Victorian age which may provide opportunities for designing.

A

B

The Year 7 pupils in photograph **C** are looking at a map showing the layout of a theme park called the 'Enviropark'. The pupils use the map to identify needs and opportunities for designing. The poster in photograph **D** has been designed by a pupil who identified the need for publicity for the Enviropark. Note the use of the computer-generated lettering to produce clear, neat text.

The pupils in photograph **E** have been looking into the possibility of designing an adventure playground for the Enviropark. They have built a model to show their ideas. An actual playground could be built as a school and community enterprise project, using the ideas proposed here.

Electronics

The photographs on these pages show electronic products made by Year 7 and Year 8 pupils.

Photograph **A** shows products made by Year 7 pupils as an introduction to electronic circuits. The circuit they have used consists of an LED (light-emitting diode) and a limiting resistor, connected to a battery. The theme of the 'Mr Men' has been chosen by the pupils as a focus for the activity.

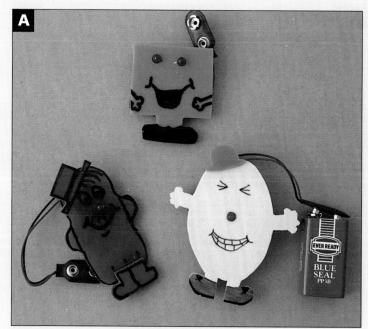

A

B

Photographs **B** and **C** show novelty items made by Year 7 pupils, using a simple circuit built on to a PCB (printed circuit board). The whole class was shown how to produce a PCB that incorporated a push button, or a switch, and two LEDs. They then went on to design some form of novelty item that enabled them to make use of the electronics skills and knowledge that they had learned. In photograph **B**, the 'Coke person' was modelled first in cardboard, before being made in thin plywood. The LED eyes light up when it is switched on. The 'felt friendlys' in photograph **C** have the circuit boards inside them, so that squeezing their tummies makes their eyes light up.

C

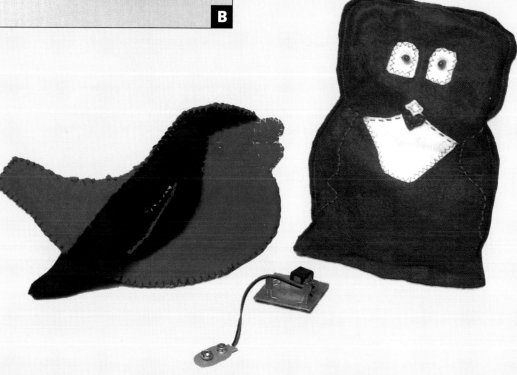

D

Photograph **D** shows a moisture tester that is used to find out if the soil in the plant pot needs watering. This has been made by a Year 8 pupil who used acrylic for the flower petals and formed polystyrene for the battery holder. The LED in the centre of the flower tells you when the plant needs some water.

The egg timers in photograph **E** were the result of a design exercise. The Year 9 pupils were asked to design a decorative piece of kitchen equipment, using a pre-prepared PCB.

You can find out more about how to make products using electronics in Chapter 8 of *Design & Technology: Techniques and Resources*.

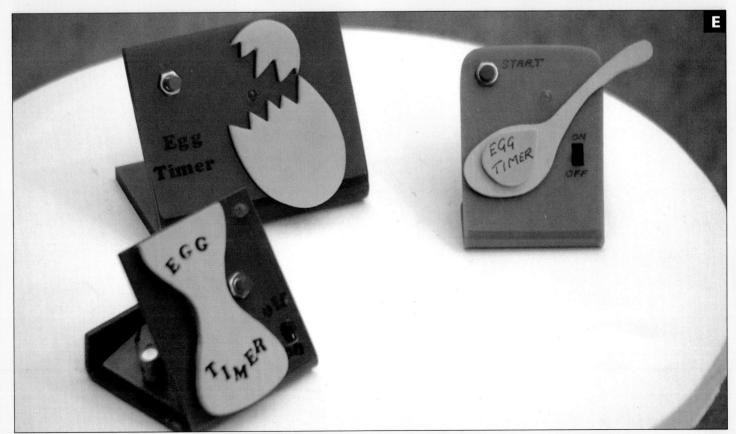

E

The Family Peace Loaf

Some Year 9 pupils decided to investigate the possibility of producing a half-white, half-brown loaf of bread. This decision was based upon some initial market research regarding people's preferences for either white or brown bread. The research was carried out amongst family and friends. The pupils came to the conclusion that many women preferred brown bread, but most men preferred white. This provided them with the challenge to create a unique loaf in order to keep the 'family peace'.

Photograph **A** shows some of the pupils outside their local supermarket which they visited to do some research.

Photograph **B** shows the pupils investigating different manufacturers' bread products inside the supermarket. They looked at the promotion techniques, pricing and packaging.

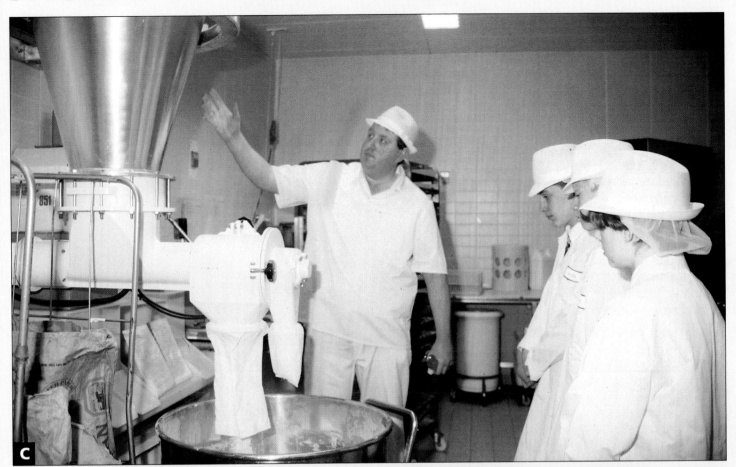

Photographs **C** and **D** show the pupils inside the store's bakery. In photograph **C**, they are being shown one of the large machines that the bakery uses. In photograph **D**, the pupils are watching freshly baked bread rolls being taken out of one of the ovens. In the bakery, loaves and rolls are baked in batches. The size of the batch must be large enough to keep the shelves stocked, but small enough to ensure that the bread is always fresh.

Back at school, the pupils carefully considered the possible ingredients for their bread before finally deciding on the recipe they wanted to use. They baked a few loaves as prototypes. Photograph **E** shows one of the pupils removing a prototype loaf from the oven, and photograph **F** shows the half-white, half-brown loaf more clearly. The pupils encountered various problems with the production of the loaves – white and brown bread have different rising rates and they need different baking times. This meant that they had to redesign and develop their recipe by adjusting the ingredients. Unfortunately, they found that this altered the texture and taste of the bread.

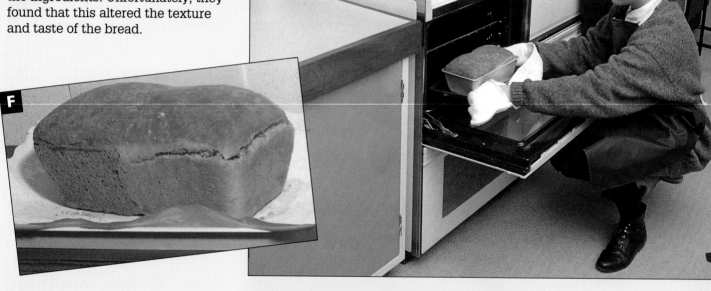

One of the pupils took a prototype loaf and detailed proposals to a product development meeting at the supermarket. Photograph **G** shows this meeting in progress. Decisions about the marketing of new products are made at this meeting. The following issues are discussed: the target market, the cost of production, the packaging and, of course, the price of the product.

Photograph **H** shows a group of pupils seeking consumer opinion on their new loaf. This is known as sampling. Once they had collected some information, they knew what people thought about their product, and they were able to modify it to try to satisfy their targeted market. At this stage, they also began to consider promoting the product. They chose the name 'Family Peace' and the slogan 'Keep all the family happy' (see photograph **I**).

The pupils' evaluation of the project led them to the conclusion that it is not really feasible to produce white and brown bread together in one loaf. The pupils then investigated alternatives, and discussed these with the product development team at the supermarket. They considered baking white and brown loaves separately, cutting them in half and then packaging the halves together. However, they discovered that this would require major changes in the production process of the bakery, as well as expensive changes in equipment. The pupils concluded that the way forward could be to investigate packaging together a small white and a small brown loaf. This could be supported with an advertising and promotion campaign.

The pupils who were engaged in this activity had a lot of fun, and learned a great deal about the business aspects of manufacturing and marketing fresh food products. They also learned how large organisations, such as supermarkets, actually work.

Family Peace

Keep all the family happy

Information Technology

The photographs on these pages show products made by Year 8 and Year 9 pupils using Information Technology (IT).

IT can be used to produce exciting graphic results. Photographs **A**, **B** and **C** show posters that have been designed by Year 8 pupils, using a computer to create the text and the graphic designs. The posters shown in photographs **A** and **B** have been created using a paint program. The pupils have used colour to create interesting effects and make a visual impact. Photograph **C** shows a poster displaying a photograph. In order to be able to use a photograph in a computer art program, the photograph needs to be filmed with a video camera that can take still photographs. Then a video digitiser changes the photograph into a format that the computer can handle, and it is fed into the computer. The size and shape of the photograph can then be altered to whatever the designer wishes.

A

B

C

Many different text styles (typefaces) can be produced using a computer. If you look at commercial posters, you will find that there are not many different typefaces on one poster. When the pupils designed the posters shown in photographs **A**, **B** and **C**, they were experimenting with many typefaces, without giving much thought to the visual impact this would create.

If you look closely at the posters, you will see that they are made from more than one sheet of paper, as most printers cannot cope with large sheets. Each sheet has part of the poster design on it, so that the sheets can be put together to form the whole poster. This is called 'tile' printing.

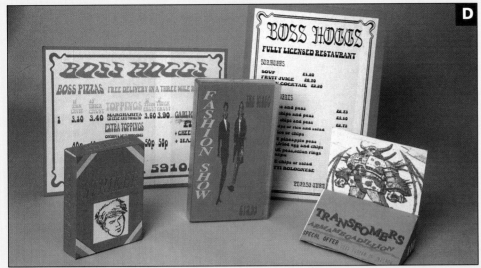

Some of the products shown in photograph **D** have been produced as flat nets, and then folded to produce three-dimensional objects. Digitised images have been used to add life to the video cover. The Boss Hoggs pizza advertisement is another example of too many typefaces and different colours being used together.

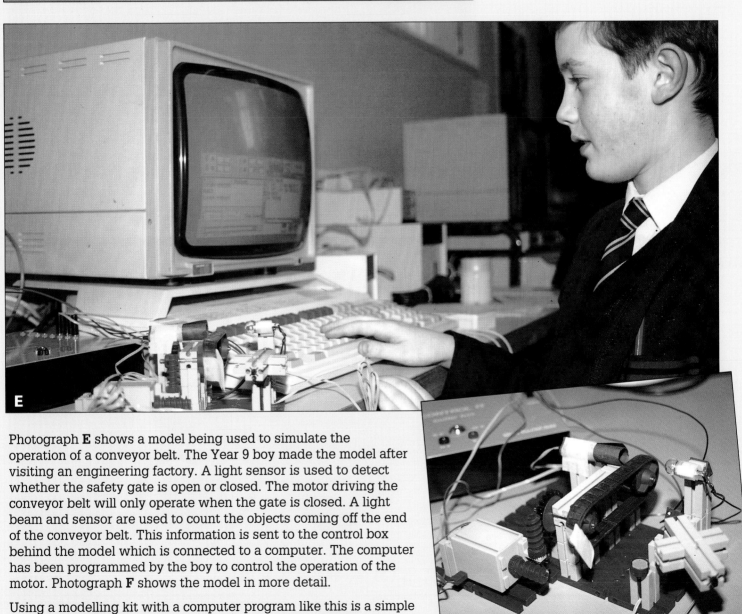

Photograph **E** shows a model being used to simulate the operation of a conveyor belt. The Year 9 boy made the model after visiting an engineering factory. A light sensor is used to detect whether the safety gate is open or closed. The motor driving the conveyor belt will only operate when the gate is closed. A light beam and sensor are used to count the objects coming off the end of the conveyor belt. This information is sent to the control box behind the model which is connected to a computer. The computer has been programmed by the boy to control the operation of the motor. Photograph **F** shows the model in more detail.

Using a modelling kit with a computer program like this is a simple way of testing whether a system will work or not. A successful program could then be used on the actual control equipment in a factory.

Celebration

The photographs on these pages show the products resulting from various activities on the theme of celebration.

Photographs **A** and **B** show the result of an activity for Valentine's Day. As you can see, the pizza has been made in the shape of a heart. The box to contain the pizza has been made with the same loving care as the contents. Computer-generated hearts and clip art have been used to give a very professional look to the box. The Year 9 pupils who were involved in this activity were also involved in a marketing exercise to cost and produce a number of Valentine pizzas to sell at school on Valentine's Day. They produced spreadsheets which they used in the costing process.

A

B

Photograph **C** shows Year 9 pupils making cards and an information folder for the Islamic festival of Eid ul-Fitr. This is a Muslim festival that celebrates the end of Ramadan, a month of fasting. The cards form part of the celebrations.

Photograph **D** shows some of the products made by a Year 7 group who have been using Christmas as a celebration theme. As well as making cards, they made presents which were sold at a school charity event. The decoration on the chocolate box has been designed on a computer, while felt-tip pens have been used to create the background colour. One group of pupils used airbrush instead, to produce an even-textured colour. The chocolates were made in a mould which was formed from polystyrene. The photograph also shows some of the pupils' design work.

The theme of celebration can lead to a wide variety of interesting Design & Technology activities.

ACKNOWLEDGEMENTS

The publishers would like to thank Anne Bridger and Cathy Burrill for their advice; Alison Sturman for supplying the Enviropark project; and Katy and Alice Bradbury for supplying pupils' handwriting.

The publishers would like to thank the following schools for their help with location photography:

Gladesmore Community School, Tottenham (Head of Technology: Cathy Burrill; Pupils: Junior Armstrong, Songul Arslan, Ganesh Bathmanathan, Hapsa Begum, Lesmi Begum, Nashir Bham, Lee Bloomfield, Leigh Clarke, Natalie Clarke, Sally Day, Ian Evans, Liza Galea, Serena Griffith, Gerina Heirs, Bobby Holmes, Nurul Islam, Sarah Maynard, Emma McLean, Ismail Patel, Rasheda Pandor, Elena Rouvas, Christopher Storey, Anthony Worrell); Northwood School, Hillingdon (Head of Technology: Jon Lambert; Pupils: Brian Abbey, Angela Beaumont, James Cheal, Carina Elliott, Frances Hayter, Aaron Lattin).

The publishers would like to thank the following schools for supplying the products photographed in chapter 8:

Banovallum School, Horncastle; Carre's Grammar School, Sleaford; Cherry Willingham Comprehensive School, Cherry Willingham; The Earl of Scarbrough High School, Skegness; Gladesmore Community School, Tottenham; King Edward VI School, Louth; Lincoln Christ's Hospital School, Lincoln; Matthew Humberstone School, Cleethorpes; The Middlefield School, Gainsborough; Queen Elizabeth's Grammar School, Horncastle; St Hugh's C of E School, Grantham; William Farr C of E Comprehensive School, Welton.

The publishers would like to thank the following for permission to reproduce photographs (the name is followed by the figure number, which is followed, where necessary, by (t) top, (b) bottom, (l) left, (r) right, (m) middle):

Arcaid/Richard Bryant 3.19; Aerofilms 7.3a; B & Q Plc 4.26; Graham Bradbury 3.6, 6.11; Britax 6.15; British Gas Plc 7.21; British Standards Institution 2.12, 6.1; British Telecommunications Museum 1.4(r), 6.17(bl, br); Child Accident Prevention Trust 7.15; Sally & Richard Greenhill 1.3, 1.17, 2.9, 2.15, 5.1(m), 5.3; Greenpeace 7.14; Robert Harding Associates 7.13, 7.19; Hulton Picture Company 6.17(tl); IBM UK Ltd 6.14; KVO Associates Ltd 7.24; Steve Lillie 6.17(tr); Magnet Plc 3.21; Mansell Collection 2.14, 3.5, 7.9, 7.29; Metrocentre, Gateshead 7.4; Milton Keynes Development Corporation 7.3b; MIRA 7.16; Network 5.1(t, r); Oracle 2.11; Path Group Plc: 'On' products (Amadeus media system, CD flip files, CD-Bars), Tape Taxi and Case Logic 1.13; Photofusion 5.1(l); Jeremy Rendell Photography/Times Network System 2.10; Sony Manufacturing Company UK 1.9; Scottish Tourist Board/Still Moving Picture Company 4.14; Peter Sharp 6.12; TechSoft UK Ltd 3.22, 3.23, 3.24, 3.25; John Walmsley 3.15, 5.1(b), 5.4a, 5.4b; Elizabeth Whiting Associates 4.25; Zefa 1.4(l), 1.16, 1.18, 4.2, 4.21, 7.1, 7.2, 7.5, 7.6, 7.11a, 7.11b, 7.17, 7.18, 7.20, 7.26, 7.28, 7.30(l, r).